A TOUCH OF CLASS

A TOUCH OF CLASS

Clive King

THE BODLEY HEAD
LONDON

1 3 5 7 9 10 8 6 4 2

Copyright © Clive King 1995

Clive King has asserted his right under the Copyright, Designs and Patents Act, 1988 to be identified as the author of this work

First published in the United Kingdom 1995
by The Bodley Head Children's Books
Random House, 20 Vauxhall Bridge Road, London SW1V 2SA

Random House Australia (Pty) Limited
20 Alfred Street, Milsons Point, Sydney,
New South Wales 2061, Australia

Random House New Zealand Limited
18 Poland Road, Glenfield,
Auckland 10, New Zealand

Random House South Africa (Pty) Limited
PO Box 337, Bergvlei 2012, South Africa

Random House UK Limited Reg. No. 954009

A CIP record for this book is available from the British Library

ISBN 0 370 31919 2

Phototypeset by Intype, London
Printed and bound in Great Britain by Mackays of Chatham PLC, Kent

THE CONFIDENTIAL DIARY OF P.N-J

Friday May 22nd

'At one time great culprits were fastened to four horses, a limb to each horse, and the horses being urged different ways, pulled limb from limb. The last person who so suffered in Europe was Robert François Damiens, for an attempt on the life of Louis XV, in 1757.'

(Found this in an old reference book.) Well, tough on Robert, but it sounds about right for *horse-rustlers* – there's yet another story about them in the local paper.

Mind you, they'd have a job to rustle our biters and bolters at Rushby Livery Stable. All the same shouldn't I get my darling Henry freeze-dried? Deep-frozen? No, it's freeze-branded, isn't it? They freeze identity numbers onto their skins, I don't think it hurts or anything. Perhaps I ought to get it done before it's too late.

But what sort of people would steal horses like this? They must be *sub-human*!

1

Dawn Raid

(Jeff's story)

'You know the old church at Rushby, don't you?'

'Me? I don't know any old churches.'

'Listen, Jeff! You know the pub, after the road across the marshes that's all bends, the Crown, isn't it?'

'I think so.'

'Can't miss it. Turn off by the post office – no, well, it's not a post office no more, but it used to be, know what I mean? Go on past some farms and there's a bit of a down and an up, and there's the church. Can't miss it.'

'Can't I?'

'Course not. You'll be coming out from Yarmouth on that motorbike of yours won't you?'

'Right.'

'Don't you go no further than the church on that noisy thing. People like to sleep at half past three in the morning. Stay at the church and keep quiet. I'll meet you there. The goods are at the stables, and there'll be this girl to help us. OK? See you Saturday then!'

That's how the telephone call had gone, hadn't it? And here I was.

But had it? And where was I?

I tried to remember exactly what Stan White had said over the phone. Half past three in the morning? It was summer, and it was warm enough and getting light, but he could have been joking. I'd sometimes stayed up that late but never got up so early.

Stan White ran a transport business and I'd done a job or two for him. Like filing the serial number off a chassis frame. Takes time, and there's nothing wrong with using a file is there? Stan paid me well enough and I never asked too many questions about his 'transport' jobs. I don't think he was all that clever at them – how he even found his way to anywhere I don't know. Had he got the name of the pub right? And the time? He'd said these long-distance jobs always start early, else you never get to the other end on time. And he'd said he needed my experience. Well, that's right, I'm good on motors. You name it, I'll start it and drive it. I like the sound of engines. Now that I'd killed the bike's motor, I didn't like the quiet. I started worrying.

Had I taken the right turning? What about that post office? How can you tell something's been a post office? And here was a grotty old church, but was it the right one? I could see the tops of two others from where I was standing. And I could only see two houses. What did they *do* with all those old churches? Don't tell me. They buried country people there. After they'd died, usually, I suppose.

No, this isn't a ghost story or anything like that. I don't believe in – *What was that*?

Something glided round the end of the church, a white thing with big staring eyes. It flapped past me, dead silent.

Oh well, could be one of those owls, I suppose, I'm no birdwatcher. But I wasn't staying there any longer. Stan had said the stable was a bit further on past the

3

church. I thought I'd check it out. I padlocked the bike to a stone cross on a grave. It wasn't really mine, that bike, but it was a good one. I might need it again and I didn't want it nicked by one of these country people, dead or alive. Not that anyone seemed to be alive here. I walked on down the lane with steep banks, where I couldn't see any houses at all. Things made noises in the trees and bushes. I wished I'd brought my walkman to listen to.

Stan had said there'd be a girl at the stable. Why did we need a girl to help us? Still, that was something to look forward to perhaps. I was sort of between girl friends. Zandra had walked out on me on the Golden Mile.

I went past a couple of farms, one smellier than the other. I suppose most of the smell was cow. The nastier smell was probably pig. I don't know how people can live in the country, it stinks. I followed my nose, like people say. I didn't know what I was looking for but now my nose was telling me something – horse. That's an animal I do know a bit about. I'll tell you how come.

My grandpa's keen on the horses, never misses a race meeting at Yarmouth, and he sometimes takes me there. He put me onto this job at Newmarket. 'Big money at Newmarket,' he said. 'Arab sheeks, rolling in it.' I got the job, straight from school. I think Grandad expected me to send him racing tips from the horses' mouths, but I wasn't allowed near that end of any horse. I don't know what I thought I'd be doing – taking the winnings to the bank, perhaps, and helping myself. But they paid me peanuts, and you know what they made me do? *Muck out*! I told them I didn't want to be a toilet attendant, not even to a Derby winner, and I quit after my first pay packet. Well, and there was this Jaguar that went for a gallop with me, too. I knew I'd rather work with motors than animals then.

I didn't much like what my nose was telling me now, but the smell meant stables, and that was where Stan had said the goods would be. Perhaps when he'd said he needed my experience, he meant with horses? No, everyone knows I'm good with motors. Well, anyway, this was a job, and there ought to be money at the end of it. Mr White's trucks were always falling to pieces but he ran a new Mercedes for himself. He had the lolly all right.

The sun wasn't up yet – it had more sense – but there was this bright moon making black shadows. I walked off the road into a yard, then into the spooky shadow of a big barn. A long white face turned towards me, and it sort of laughed at me through its nose.

It's all right, it's a horse, I told myself. This should be the place then. There had been quite a few farms but this was the first stable. I walked past the stall and the horse stretched its neck out at me and made its noise again. 'Oh no you don't,' I said. I know enough about horses not to trust them, either end.

I came out into the moonlight into another yard. There was a big old square van parked there. Stan White's? Could be. And the other side of the yard was a row of horse faces, each one looking at me from the black open top of a doorway.

So I had a look at the van. The cab wasn't locked and I climbed in. My foot trod on something that went crunch and I sat in something cold and wet. Yuk! They'd been having a picnic there and hadn't cleared up the crisps and coke cans. The controls told me it was a Bedford diesel job at least nine years old. Not brilliant, but I could manage it. Starter key? No,

5

they were not that careless. But I could manage that too if I had to.

I got down and had a look at the loading arrangements. A little door in one side. I didn't see the use of that. I got it open and looked in. A little room with clothes hanging up. Did someone live there? I walked round the back of the van. Rear loader, one big door, hinges at the bottom, closed with clamps. I undid the clamps, pulled at the big door, and I just got out in time before it clonked me on the head. It made a sort of ramp. Well, I'm not stupid, I could see that a horse could walk up it and get inside. I could tell by the smell and by what was on the floor there had been horses in there. The space was divided up by a couple of partitions, so there was room for only three horses.

Well, that was the transport. A horse box. So Stan's goods had to be horses. I thought I'd better have a look at them. Not too close, though. I counted, and there seemed to be nine of them.

It wasn't like Newmarket, because they came in all sizes, big'uns and little'uns. One was so small it could hardly look over the half door. But plenty of meat on all of them, not skinny like those racers. They all looked tame enough and they made sniffling noises as if they wanted something. Breakfast, I suppose. I wished I hadn't thought of that. I felt hungry myself.

I got back into the cab and looked to see if there was anything to eat. Only the half empty bag of crisps I'd put my mucky boot on, and I wasn't that hungry. I sat there and waited.

And waited. And thought.

And I thought, well, here I am with a truck I can drive, and a load of horses I could drive off with. They said about Stan White that he wasn't too keen on paying for what he collected, nor delivering what he was paid for. I wouldn't put it past him to set up a bit of horse rustling. But if he didn't turn up why should I wait for him? Talk about temptation! I wasn't sure what I could do with a load of horses, but I knew that any animal was worth something, even if it wasn't good enough to interest an oil sheikh.

Can you blame me? I thought I'd have a go.

I had a look at the partitions in the back of the lorry. It was a bit dark inside but it didn't take me long to suss out how to unbolt them and swing them open so the first horse could go in the one nearest the cab. I tell you, that sort of thing's no problem for me, anything mechanical. But animals are different. Me, I'm pretty cool, usually, but the old heart began thumping when I walked up to the stalls. I told myself there's nothing to it. A horse has got four legs. You don't have to lift it or anything. You pull it along and it goes where you want it to go – dead easy! I was wrong.

Hanging outside the stalls were those things you put round horses' heads to lead them, with ropes clipped on. I'd got to get the hang of that first. I picked one up and tried to remember how the lads at Newmarket had put them on. They'd had posher ones there but these seemed to work the same. You got the horse's nose through that loop and you buckled the long strap over the top of its head. Head-collar, that's what they call it.

I looked into a stall in the middle of the row. This horse was standing away from the door, so I could get in without pushing past it. I shut the door behind me so it couldn't run away. And there I was, in this dark smelly place, alone with this – this *beast*. It looked all right, pretty glossy, almost like one of those race horses, and I reckoned it was worth a bit.

You're supposed to talk to horses, aren't you,

7

though I don't believe they understand a word you say. I felt pretty stupid saying, 'Right, you and me are going places, girl.' She – yes, I do know the facts of life and I'd had a look underneath and checked that out – she didn't say a word, but stood there nice and quiet. I held out the head-collar, ready to slip it on. She didn't buck or rear or roll her eyes or lay her ears back or do any of the freaky things I'd seen horses do. She just turned her head and bit me on the arm, hard. Even through my leather jacket, that hurt!

I got to the door, let myself out quick and stood in the yard rubbing my arm and saying what I thought about females. I couldn't think of a bad enough word. 'You – you *Zandra*!' I said to her.

Was it worth going on? I don't like giving up on something once I've started. There were eight other horses to choose from. Maybe they didn't all eat people for breakfast.

I walked to the far end of the row of stalls. There was a big old horse there with its head over the door. It looked quiet enough, but then so had the other one. I had an idea and fetched the squashed crisp packet from the horse-box. I chose the biggest bit of crisp and held it out to the horse. It made a sudden grab – not at me but the crisp packet, chewed it for a bit and spat the wrapping onto the ground. Then it looked at me asking for more. I reckoned I'd made a friend.

'Come along then, mate,' I said. 'We'll find you lots of crisps.' I patted its neck. Perhaps I could get the head-collar on as it looked over the door. I tried to get the loop over its nose, but it was too tight. It turned its head to me, not to bite but to rub its nose on my shoulder. I loosened the noseband thing, slipped it on, reached up and buckled the strap over the top of its head. It was on! But my heart was bumping as I unbolted the stable door to lead it out. What would it do now?

'Out you come then, er—'

Boy or girl? I peered underneath. Boy – or what was left of one after the vet had done his work.

He was standing there on three legs, lifting up one of his front feet.

'Oh no, you're not *begging* are you?' This was a real old wally. I'd struck lucky this time.

I pulled on the leading rope and led him towards the horse-box. He pulled round a bit and seemed to want to go towards the open gate to the meadow, but I wasn't having that.

'Come on, boy! We're going for a drive.'

I led him to the ramp of the horsebox. He stopped dead and blew his nose and the snot went into my face. I tugged at the rope. He went backwards. The harder I tugged the faster he reversed. There was a muck-heap and a ditch by it, and I thought he was going backwards into that. But he plunged his head down and whipped round and pulled me over into the muck.

He clattered away towards the gate, and as I lay there swearing I heard someone laughing.

No, it wasn't a horse laugh this time. You might even say it was sort of silvery. Still, I don't like people laughing at me. I got up and tried to brush myself down, and got muck all over my hands. There was nothing to wipe them on except the dry part of my jeans.

'Are you all right?' a girl's voice asked. Where was she? I looked along the line of stables and there was this human face, alongside a white pony's, just peering over a half door.

'No,' I answered.

She wasn't very big. I usually like them taller. But the face over the door looked all right, I suppose.

'Why have you put Nelson out?' she asked. 'He hasn't had his breakfast.'

'Tough!' I said. 'He's chewed a crisp packet and he seems to be doing all right on the grass.'

'Better shut the gate then, we'll never catch him again.' I don't like bossy girls but I walked to the gate and shut it. I felt a bit cooler when I'd walked back to the stable where the girl stood. I peered over the door. Well, it was a girl all right, like Stan had said there would be, but there wasn't much of her to look at. She was doing something to the pony's back end with a sponge.

'Stan said you'd be here,' I said.

'Shut up, you *pain*!' she said. Rude as well as bossy! 'Will you *stand*, Henry?' she went on.

'My name's not Henry,' I said, sharpish. 'It's Jeffrey.'

'I was talking to the pony.' She looked up and smiled. Nice smile. 'I'm Trish. Who's Stan?'

'The guy who said you'd be here.'

'Oh?' she muttered, bending over to pick muck out of the pony's hoof. 'Foot! Good boy! Well, we've got a driver, great! And you're good and early. We were worried we wouldn't get there, weren't we, Henry darling?' And she gave the pony a kiss on its nose. Something already told me they had a sort of stormy relationship, this Trish and Henry. I felt a bit left out, but she smiled up at me again.

'We won't be long. I've just got to get his bandages on,'

'Is he sick, then?' I asked. She just went off in that silvery laugh as if I'd made a joke, and started grubbing around on the floor, wrapping the animal's legs up with thick wadding and yards of red bandage.

10

'Do you think you can get the van started?' her voice came up from the floor.

'Of course I can,' I said. 'Have you got the key?'

'No,' she gasped, sounding worried. 'Haven't you?'

'Not to worry,' I said. 'No problem.' Well, I hoped there wasn't.

I had a few tools in my pockets, wirecutters, screwdriver and that. I always carry them. Never know when they'll come in useful. It was easy enough to get behind the wobbly old dashboard, with its spider's web of electric leads. There were spiders there and all. I snipped a few wires and crossed them. *Tick tick tick*, the pump came up to pressure. *Err err err err*, the starter churned over. The engine didn't start. Give it a rest and try again. *Err err err*! The engine fired and turned. A cloud of blue smoke drifted from the back of the van until I could hardly see ahead. Could I stop it if I needed? I disconnected the wires, and there was silence. That was all right, then.

When I got back to the stable the pony looked like a real nasty accident, wrapped in all his bandages and a rug. The girl was actually wrapping a bandage round his tail!

'Is that a specially *valuable* pony then, that you have to gift-wrap him?' I asked, sarcastic.

'Of course you're speshly vallabul, aren't you darling?' she crooned, stroking Henry's neck. All this lovey-dovey stuff made me feel a bit sick, on an empty stomach and all. Time was getting on and there was sunshine out on the marsh, and here we were messing around with this one middling-size pony.

'I mean, worth more than the others here?' I asked, with a bit of the old acid in my voice.

Then she gave me a real hard look. 'Could be. You're talking about Kingsvale Hautbois, you know!'

'No, I meant Henry.'

11

'Same animal. We're ready! Open the door and stand aside!'

I opened the door for her but I wasn't in a hurry to stand aside. That animal shot through the doorway like a rocket! I jumped back in time to save myself being knocked over, and the girl just managed to pull the pony up on the leading rope.

'Always like this with doorways!' she grinned. 'Got a thing about them. Had a difficult birth, or something.'

She led the pony to the ramp of the horsebox. Henry didn't seem to mind the idea of getting aboard, in fact he thundered up the ramp as fast as he'd shot out of the stable. Trish followed on the end of the lead rope and tied it to a ring.

'Shut the partition, will you?' I did that. The catch was stiff and nicked a bit out of my finger.

'Pass me up the haynet!'

'The what?'

'*Haynet*!' She pointed to a net full of hay. I lifted it. It was dripping with water that soaked my jeans. I passed it up to her and she hung it up by the pony's head. She shut the other partitions and came down the ramp.

'Right,' she said. 'Tack, tack-box, hat, jacket, haynet, water, bucket, boots, whip, body protector, lunchbox, jumper, *pony*!' She reeled this off like a sort of magic spell, and ticked things off on her fingers. I hadn't a clue what it all meant, but this girl seemed to know what she was doing. What *was* she doing? It all seemed to be out of my hands. But Stan White seemed to have picked a good one.

'Help me get the ramp up!' she ordered.

But I rebelled at that. 'What about the others?' I asked.

'What others?'

12

'There's room for two more horses.'

'But Henry's the only one going, from here. Hurry up, he doesn't like standing alone.'

Henry seemed to be trying to dig his way out through the floor of the box. The girl heaved upwards on the heavy door. I gave up protesting and yanked it upwards, then pushed it shut, and we fastened the clamps.

'Let's go,' she said.

We got into the cab. I fiddled with the wires. The engine fired. There were more clouds of blue smoke. I shoved the gear lever, released the clutch, and the creaking old van ground forward.

Trish settled back on the beat-up seat of the cab and closed her eyes as if she was tired. I had to keep mine open, looking at the road. At least I was in control now, in the driving seat. Here I was, alone with this female person. Even Henry was tucked away in the back and couldn't see us. I had no idea where we were going, though, or how the whole thing would end up.

'Which way?' I asked casually.

She opened her eyes. Green ones.

'Didn't they tell you? Beech Farm. We pick up Jennie and Ellie and Butch and Digger.' This wasn't such good news.

'Are those people or horses?' I had to ask. I didn't fancy picking up two guys called Butch and Digger.

'Two of each,' she said. And she shut her eyes again.

'Er – just remind me of the best way to Beech Farm,' I said. I'd never heard of it, of course, but I thought I would play cunning, and not give too much away. I had this feeling that she thought I was some-one I wasn't.

13

'I thought you knew. Go right here, left, left, right past the church, then second right. It's no distance.'

That was clear enough. She dozed off again, and it gave me time to get used to the controls. And to take a look at the girl now and then. Old tracksuit with stable stains, which couldn't give much away about the figure underneath. Skinny, I guessed, though there were bumps in the right places. Straw-coloured hair all over the place. Lace-up ankle boots, ugly and hard. She didn't exactly smell of money, know what I mean? Nor did she really smell of sex. I don't have to tell you what she did smell of, especially those boots.

We had come a different way round to the church where I'd left the bike. I slowed right down, and the girl opened her eyes. That improved her face a lot.

'What are you stopping here for?'

'My bike. I left it here.'

'There won't be room for a bike. Pick it up when we come back.'

Who said we'd be coming back? But the bike wasn't mine, so what did it matter, and then I thought I'd better not hang around this meeting place. I didn't *want* to meet Stan White, not now. With any luck I could do the thing my way. We went on to the second right and came to a farm entrance.

The girl said, 'In there!', as if I ought to know, and I turned in a bit too quickly. The horsebox rocked.

'Go easy!' she snapped. 'Poor Henry, in the back there!'

Two big girls were standing in the farm yard. They were waving. No, they weren't, they were holding up their hands and flapping them, making signs that didn't mean welcome. Trish put her head out of the cab window.

'Stop! Don't come any further! Go away!' the big girls called out.

14

One of them put her fingers round her own neck. 'Strangles!' she hollered.

'They don't seem to want us,' I said. 'Funny friends you've got!'

'Oh *no!*' Trish called through the window. 'Rotten luck! See you Jennie! See you Ellie!' Then she said to me, 'You'd better back out. We don't want Henry to catch it, do we?'

If those girls had got it, whatever it was, I supposed we didn't. Pity! One of them looked real sexy. But I was too busy backing out into the lane to ask what all that was about.

'Where now?' I asked.

She pointed back past the church and said, 'Norwich. We'll just have to take Henry by himself. He's all right alone so long as we keep going.'

But this time I pulled up at the church.

'I'm going to get that bike aboard,' I said. 'Then Henry will have company.'

'He may not *like* it,' the girl protested.

'The bike may not like him,' I said. 'But let's try.'

She sulked, but she couldn't do anything about it. We got down from the cab and opened the ramp door. Henry started dancing and the girl had to quieten him. I fetched the bike and wheeled it to the ramp, but it was too heavy to push up. So I had to start the engine in spite of the girl's protests. I got it chugging quietly up the ramp and into its stall. Henry looked over at it, sort of interested.

'He likes it,' I said.

We put the ramp up and drove away again. On the B road towards Norwich the old horsebox settled down to a steady forty. However much I pushed the pedal down it didn't seem to want to go any faster. But that was all right. It gave me a chance to sort things out.

15

The girl was looking at me more closely now.

'You're not Monica's uncle, are you?' It wasn't a question, the way she said it.

'I'm not Monica's uncle, nor the monkey's uncle, nor nobody's uncle,' I said. It didn't seem to be much use pretending I was.

'Never mind, I'm just glad to have a driver,' she said. 'Look, I'm starving. Did you bring breakfast or have you had it?'

She opened a lunch bag, the sort that little kids take to school with Snoopy on it, and took out a packet of crisps. She opened it and I held out my left hand for some.

'Keep your hands on the wheel,' she said. 'I know the steering's dodgy, and you're not used to it, are you?' She fed crisps into my mouth and hers, bacon-flavour. On bumpy bits of the road I got a nibble of female finger, stable-flavour. Yummy!

'Well, what's the programme then?' I really wanted to know.

'Trials.'

My guts turned over. It's a word I don't like.

'*Trials*!' I choked. 'You're joking! You have to be nicked first, and remanded and that.' I know about these things. 'What sort of trials?'

Her turn to choke – with laughing. She seemed to think I was a real comic.

'Well, for starters, there's—' and she said something I didn't get, through a splutter of bacon crisps.

'What's dress-arse?' I asked. That's what it sounded like. It set her off laughing again. But I tried to be serious.

'Is there cash in it?' I asked.

She calmed down. 'Hopefully. And of course the better they do the better you can sell them on.'

Ah, well, I didn't want to go on asking questions

16

and looking ignorant. I didn't know what Stan's plan had been but this girl seemed to have some good ideas.

The traffic got thicker after we turned onto the A road to Norwich, and I was kept busy driving that van. Not too many cars ahead of us, but a look in the mirror showed a tail growing behind, and the back of my neck could just about feel the bad vibes from the drivers who couldn't get past. Forty miles an hour on a good road! I tried accelerating down a dip but the whole van shook and the girl told me to slow down.

There was a lay-by on the right. Parked in it, facing the way we'd come, was a big old cattle truck. The cover of the engine was open and a man had his head inside. Propped against the cab was a sour-looking girl. And walking impatiently up and down was a tubby man . . .

'Can you steer?' I said quickly to Trish.

'Yes. No! What do you mean—?'

I grabbed her right hand and put it on the steering wheel. I ducked down below the dashboard.

'Got a loose wire, I think!'

I felt the van swerve, and I heard *paaauurp*! from a car coming towards us and a bit of a thump from inside the van, but the girl managed to straighten up and carry on. I bobbed up again, and we were past the lay-by. That tubby man couldn't have seen me. I didn't want him to. It was Stan.

The girl was pale and furious. 'Don't you *ever* do that again! You should have stopped!'

I grinned at her. 'You did well, baby! I like a girl who don't panic.'

'I hope that thump was your bloody bike, not Henry,' she said, and then sat silent, over on her side of the cab seat, glaring at me. A pity, after we had

17

been getting on so well together. Then she said, 'Aren't you a bit young to be driving a lorry like this?'

'Aren't you a bit young to be out alone with a guy like me?' I came back at her.

'I could be older than I look, couldn't I?'

'Me too, perhaps.'

'You'll have to do, anyway. I've just *got* to get Henry to Burlingham today. It's a very important event and I can't miss it. But I want him there in one piece, see?'

'So what's the big event?'

'It's a one day open.'

She seemed to like stringing ordinary words together so they meant rubbish. *Dress-arse. One day open.* We were getting nowhere, or rather we were getting into Norwich, with its roundabouts and ring roads, and I was busy driving and she was telling me which exits to take from roundabouts. But I wasn't too happy. There would be coppers in Norwich. We're not friends, me and them.

But we got round Norwich and out the other side. We took a faster road and the tail-back built up behind us again. Every now and then a Ford Sierra or a Cavalier accelerated past us, and the driver glared at me, while cars coming the other way glared with their headlights and blared with their horns.

'They can nick you for driving too *slow*, can't they?' I muttered.

And there, ahead of us, was a policeman, all white and yellow, standing in the road. This is it, I thought. No use ducking under the dashboard.

'Oh, I forgot!' said Trish, as the cars slowed down. She opened her lunch bag again and took out a strip of yellow paper which she held against the wind-screen. She waved at the copper, like she was the

Princess of Wales, and he sent her ever such a nice smile, held up the oncoming traffic, and waved us into an entrance. Trish licked the sticker and stuck it on the glass. Inside out, the writing looked like this.

ЯOTITƎPMOƆ

Magic? Anyway, it had worked.

There was short grass both sides of the truck, and tapes strung on iron stakes to make barriers, and yes, little yellow notices saying COMPETITORS PARK-ING and HORSE BOXES. It was a bit like a big open-air pop concert I'd been to, only the people here were all wearing mucky-looking wax jackets and green wellies.

Still, I felt sort of important as we drove along to the horse box park. The other vehicles put me down, though: shiny trailers towed by new Jap four-tracks, with the shiny bums of horses showing behind, and great posh vans that seemed to be mobile homes for two large families, one human and one horsey.

'I wish I'd nicked one of them instead!' I said aloud. But Trish was busy waving to some people she knew.

'This'll do,' she said to me. 'Pull up alongside that trailer.'

I did that, and killed the engine. We were there. Where were we?

THE CONFIDENTIAL DIARY OF P.N-J

Saturday May 23rd

Advance reminder: OPEN ONE-DAY EVENT BURLINGHAM
    This is the crunch, *qualifier*, must not miss!!

19

Check-list

entry fees	√	paid (only just)
horse	√	(Henry) fit (touch wood!)
tack	√	clean
clothes	√	clean, if threadbare
rider	√	(me) distracted, ought to be studying
transport	√	horse van available
driver	????	

The good news is that Jennie and Ellie will share transport and expenses, and we can hold each other's horses. Bad news: Joanna usually loves to drive to events and have a natter with mums etc but she's got to take her own old mum to hospital so we've got no driver. Says Monica's uncle will probably be willing to do it or if not he'll get hold of someone else. As if I didn't have enough to worry about with A levels to revise for and all. Roll on my driving test!

2

Big Event

There were horses coming off vans and trailers, head first, tail first and sideways.

'Quick,' said Trish. 'We've got to get Henry out.'

She jumped out her side, and I got out my side and we met round the back of the van. We released the clamps, heaved down on the ramp, and I knew enough this time to move out from under it. There was Henry, glaring at us over the partition and over the bike which had fallen against it, but no harm done. I wheeled the bike down the ramp and heard a little girl squeak, 'Mummy, Mummy, somebody's pony's got *wheels*! He! He! He!'

'Henry, darling, are you all right?' Trish crooned. He looked all right. She ran up the ramp, struggled with the partition, undid the pony's leading rope and led him down. Henry stood there for a moment, looking around at the scene, then rushed down the ramp. I kept out of the way.

'Here, you hang on to him. I've got to change,' Trish said, and handed me the rope. She opened the little door at the side, pulled out a short wooden ladder, and disappeared up into the little room. I held onto the rope and watched Henry mistrustfully. He sniffed at the bike, then put his head down and munched the squashed grass of the lorry park. He seemed quiet enough.

I had time to look around. I counted over fifty vehicles and they were still rolling in. Couldn't be less than half a million pounds worth of them. And the horses! There were some horses with riders on them already. Diddy little ponies with snotty little kids on them, giving them stick. Big glossy ones with posh riders, prancing about. I couldn't tell how much the livestock was worth. But if the owners spent so much on the transport, I reckoned the horses must be worth just as much. Anyway, this girl seemed to have brought me where the big money was, and I was grateful for that. Maybe this was the big market. But just what was in it for me?

Henry was moving from one patch of grass to another, fussy like, and towing me towards the backsides of a couple of tethered horses. Where *was* that girl?

I looked towards the horse box. At the top of the steps stood something really posh. Starting from the top, it wore a smooth black cap with a peak in front and a little bow at the back. Some blonde hair showed underneath it, neatly screwed up in a net. There was a collar and tie, like an old-fashioned gent's, and a tight jacket showing ins and outs that were definitely female. The same for the creamy, skintight, fit-to-burst bottom half. Little black boots with a polish on them like a motor-hearse. And *white gloves* – in summer! The thing that spoiled it was a big cardboard number tied round her middle with string, number 33.

I gave it my best smile. 'Hi! I said. 'Have you seen Trish?'

'Very funny!' Trish's voice came from this vision. 'Do I look all right?'

22

'You look *different*,' I had to tell her. 'Honest, I thought you were someone else. I quite liked you the way you were.'

'I didn't dress up to please *you*.' Her voice was a bit hard and nervous. 'Bring Henry here and we'll tack him up.'

I lugged Henry forward.

'*Stand*, Henry! Do you think you could get his leg-bandages off?' she asked hopefully. 'I don't want to muck up my jods.' *Jods*? Those skin-tight trousers, I supposed. The things on Henry's back legs weren't as clean as they had been when we started. I could see her problem. What had I got to lose after rolling in the stable yard? I undid the tapes and unwound the bandages on all four legs. Trish pulled off his blanket, and the bandages from his tail, and fussed around with a sponge and a brush.

'You're a dirty little sod, aren't you, Henry?' she said, as if she was used to it. 'Hold him while I get the tack down.'

A tack to me is something you don't want to get in a motor-tyre, but she brought down a shiny saddle and a bundle of leather and metal from the horsebox. 'You can hold the bridle too.'

She plonked the saddle, with its fluffy pad, on the pony's back, reached under its belly for the thick leather strap, and buckled it up tight.

'Don't it stop them breathing, that thing round their chests?' I wanted to know.

'Their ribs aren't hinged, like yours,' she said. I'd never thought about my ribs having hinges. She took the bridle from me, held the top strap up near the pony's ears, shoved her thumb into the side of his mouth and dragged the hard metal between his teeth. He sucked it and chewed on it.

'Why do they put up with it?' I asked. 'I wouldn't.'

23

'Wouldn't what?' she asked, doing up a lot of different buckles.

'Wouldn't have a thing like that in my mouth. Why do they all let you do it?'

This made her stop and think, though not for long. 'I suppose the answer is that some horses never do. Then they miss all the fun, don't they, Henry?'

Fun? There seemed to be as much fun in the air as you'd find at a funeral. People all round swearing at horses and snapping at each other.

'Right!' she said at last. 'I'll get up. Hold his head and put your weight on the other stirrup.' I didn't quite get the idea, but she put one foot in a stirrup and heaved herself on board. She was way above me and I could see up her nose. I suppose she wasn't really sneering down at me but it looked like it.

'Let him go!' she snapped. 'You can watch us in Arena B, nine-forty.'

And off they went between the lines of vehicles, to an open space where horses with riders were milling around doing nothing in particular. I was free to wander about. Not being a horse, nor on a horse, nor with a horse, I felt I was sort of invisible. At first I was amazed at all the doors of cars and cabs left open, ponies left tied up by themselves – and not a copper in sight! And then I began to notice that there was usually a bad-tempered dog in the empty car, or one family was keeping an eye on someone else's horses. It wouldn't do to take any chances. You'd get lynched.

And there was another thing. You'd be lynched by women. Females seemed to run this show. Bare-armed women at the wheels of huge lorries. Mums in sloppy jeans snapping '*Will* you get yourself *ready*?' Big beefy girls banging horses about. Spindly little girls staggering with buckets full of water. Ah, there was a bloke! But they'd put him into a hot dark suit, waistcoat, collar-and-tie, and a hat like a pisspot. *He* wasn't having a relaxed fun day either.

There was a person trying to get up on a big horse.

'I say, *would* you mind holding him?' You couldn't be sure, but I thought the voice was male. Who was he speaking to? Me?

There was nobody else so I went cautiously up to the fidgeting animal and took it by the bridle. I was learning. The guy – yes, his jeans or jods or whatever didn't have quite the smooth shape of a girl rider's, and there wasn't much of his hair showing, but otherwise they all dressed the same – anyway it climbed into the saddle.

'My pleasure, squire,' I said, pulling at my forelock. That's what the lower classes are supposed to do, isn't it?

'Thank you, peasant,' he said.

I kept hold of the bridle. There was something I wanted to ask him.

'What does a bloke have to be to join this club?' I asked. 'Some sort of wimp?'

He fixed me with a fishy grey eye and leaned down, as if he had a secret to whisper.

'I can tell you, friend. You need nerves of steel and a hide like a rhinoceros. And that's just to cope with the women. I don't recommend it.'

The twat! I should have pulled him off his high horse. But then I thought, *no, that's really cool*! I let the horse go and he rode away, po-faced.

I looked at my watch. Time to find Arena B. Oh, no direction signs or anything, you were supposed to know where things were.

There they were, Trish and Henry, walking and trotting around a bit of flat field. A bit of a gallop. No you couldn't call it that, I learnt the new word later: canter. Then Trish steered towards me. She was smiling and a lot of her nervousness was gone. She patted Henry on the neck and said, 'Well done, good *boy*!'

'When does your show start?' I asked. She seemed surprised.

'That was it, the dressage bit,' she said. 'Weren't you watching?'

What was I supposed to be watching? This place was really trying to make me feel stupid.

'Can we go home now?' I asked, sarcastic.

'Two more legs,' she said.

'Ain't four enough for him then?'

I must have looked pissed off, because she said, 'You may find the next bit more fun. We've got forty minutes before the crosscountry run. This way! I'll need you to hold him.'

I walked alongside them. Now that I was with a pony and rider I didn't feel so invisible. People actually smiled at Trish and Henry and me, and said 'How do you do?' No they didn't, they said 'How did you do?'

To one of these friends Trish answered, 'I may have scored fifty or so. Maybe better. Forty with a bit of luck.'

'Are you really trying to blow my mind?' I asked her, not too sweetly.

She seemed surprised. 'What do you mean?'

'You might tell me what's going on. How can a score of forty be better than fifty?'

'They're penalties.'

'Forty *penalties*? Sounds like the Greek football team! So what have you been doing wrong?' She looked so innocent in her clean white collar. But 40 penalties – perhaps she was human after all!

'We didn't do much wrong. That's why I'm happy. Here we are.'

We'd come to a rougher bit of the ground. There were logs and bales of straw and oil-barrels and water troughs, all with little flags on them, and even I could see that they were things to jump over. Trish put her leg over the saddle and slid to the ground. She handed me the end of the reins.

'You don't mind hanging onto him, do you? *Stand*, Henry!'

'What, again? Aren't you going to ride him?'

'No, I've got to walk it. Won't be long.' And then she ran off on her own two legs, calling out, 'Wait for me!' to a couple of other girls.

They were ganging up on me, to keep me confused! A horse show with a crosscountry run that they talked about walking but you ran it on foot and asked the others to wait for you! The girls disappeared into a little wood. Henry tugged at the reins I was holding. 'Don't you pull me around!' I told him. In spite of his mouthful of metal he was happily eating a thistle. I didn't know if it was good for him. Nobody told me anything.

And we waited. And waited. What if I just got on Henry and galloped away with him? It might be better than being – what did they call it in the cowboy films? A hitching-post?

We weren't the only ones waiting. There were two mums in jeans, hanging on to a pony each and having a natter.

One of the mums was staring at Henry.

'Isn't that Kingsvale Hautbois?' she suddenly asked me.

'Er – dunno,' was all I could say at first. But wasn't that what Trish had said back at the stable? 'Yes, I think so.'

'That's what I thought. Joanna's got him now, hasn't she? He was always a goer but he never had any brakes.'

Brakes? Now there was something I could understand. If Henry hadn't any brakes I'd better not go off on him. I was going to ask how you did fit a set of brakes to a horse when the girls came panting back, twittering about a coffin in the wood – or at least that was what it sounded like.

'Right, girls, off you go and get changed again! We'll lead the ponies back to the van.'

The girls walked off, the mums and ponies followed slowly, and Henry and I followed them. Bits of conversation drifted back from the ladies.

'Oh yes, she took her back to the stud for another go, and then my dear she kept on going back but it wasn't with the mare and now everyone says she's moving in with him. They're both in foal so I suppose that's all right . . .' Nothing but horse talk. Or was it? Who cared?

When I got back to the horsebox I was prepared for a change, but not for this butch-looking figure with shoulders like an American footballer, a rugby jersey, boots like a German officer in a movie and a helmet like a Russian tank commander. It was still Trish.

'I've got to change his bit,' she said. 'I'll need to put the brakes on this time.' At least now I'd see how that was done.

She began, 'You wouldn't mind—'

'Hanging on to him for a bit?' I finished off for her. 'Okay,' I said wearily.

She fiddled with buckles again and took one bit of ironmongery out of his mouth and put in a different shaped one. He fidgeted and she swore, '*Stand*, Henry, damn you!' but she won and he put up with it. She put an extra strap round his saddle and boots on his legs. She picked up her whip, and hesitated.

'You'd better give me a leg,' she said.

'I need both mine,' I told her.

'Oh God!' she exclaimed. She was all tensed up again. 'Look how he's doing it.' A man had got hold of a girl by her bent leg and was hoisting her onto a horse. He was probably her dad, but I didn't mind trying with Trish. She put one hand on Henry's mane and the other on the back of the saddle, cocked up her leg and I grabbed it and gave a big heave. Light as a feather! All that padding had no weight to it. In fact I nearly threw her over the other side of Henry, and he jiggled about as she got her balance.

'Whoa! Go easy, you idiots!' I noticed that. Me and Henry, both idiots.

She got her feet in the stirrups, said, 'Wish me luck!' and trotted off to where we'd just been.

'Break a leg!' I called after her. People looked round at me. No, perhaps you didn't say that to riders. I'd learned to say it from Zandra. She was on the stage, sort of, and theatre people are so superstitious that you mustn't even mention luck to them, good or bad, so you say 'Break a leg!' I didn't really want Trish to break that leg I'd held. I hoped she hadn't heard me.

Things were really happening now where those jumps were. There was rider number 30, kicking her (his?) horse towards a jump made of motor tyres. Dunlop 185/60's I guessed they were. The horse didn't like motor tyres and I don't think the rider did either. The horse slowed down. The rider hit the horse with a stick. The horse took some quick steps forward, then put his brakes on – you could see it happen. The horse stopped but the rider didn't. The red-and-white jockey cap bounced on the rubber tyres – rider's head still inside of course – and the rider did a neat headflip over onto the other side. Real clever, it must take some practice, I thought. But then the ambulance made its way through the horses and people towards the jumps. I don't like ambulances. For the first time I understood that these kids weren't playing.

I wondered if rider number 33 was going to try the same trick – and for some reason I hoped she wouldn't. Why should I care? But I did.

Rider number 32 started off on a lolloping brown horse, went slowly up to each jump, and you could see they weren't going to make it. But they did, sort of climbing over, one leg at a time. I hoped Trish wasn't going to make a fool of herself like this. Numbers 31 and 32 disappeared among the trees. It was a funny sort of race, with runners starting one after the other, quite big gaps between them.

Number 33 was away! I could see Trish pulling at the reins already, trying to put the brakes on I suppose. 'Come on, girl!' I muttered. I wanted to yell, but no one else was yelling. Henry seemed to be all for it. He sailed over the first two jumps and I could see blue sky underneath him. They came to the motor tyres. Henry seemed a bit doubtful, Trish urged him on. Henry took off vertical, like a helicopter, and before they came down I could see sky between the saddle and the girl's bum. But they were over, and she was still on top. With a bit of a whoop from Trish, they hared off into the wood. I don't know what there was in the wood – coffins? – but the next rider to come out the other end wasn't 31 or 32, it was 33. Henry was striding out like a good'un and they flew over oil-barrels, haybales, water-troughs, like – I dunno – like they were on the moon and gravity didn't count. Trish was just sitting there, steady, and they went together like a dream. Round the far end of the big field, over the final jump of telephone poles, and there they were, galloping in, a great grin on Trish's face.

They pulled up. Trish put her arms round Henry's neck, and gasped, 'Well done, boy!' I've seen people on some sort of high, often enough, and this girl was certainly riding high. Then she slid off Henry, let him stand there puffing, and gave me a great warm sweaty hug!

Well, I found that it's not all fun hugging a body-protector, that's a sort of plastic packaging that goes over all the interesting parts. And I suppose she had no one else to hug, except Henry. But it made up for some of the hanging about.

'So we've won, then?' I said to Trish. 'I mean, you've won?'

She unhugged me and looked a bit shy at letting herself go like that.

'Not yet,' she said. 'I'm in with a chance. Is it lunch time?'

I'd noticed a smell of frying onions coming from a trailer so I said. 'How about a burger and a coke? On me?'

'That would be great,' she said. 'Look, I'll see if I can put Henry in a box with Clare's pony. He'll be quiet then.'

I followed my nose to the burger trailer and got in a short queue. I looked at the prices written up – they were a real rip-off but there was nowhere else to go – and then I felt through my pockets. A handful of coins. I kicked myself and felt a real wally. Offering to treat a girl and then finding you're skint! Of course, I'd spent nearly my last ten p on a gallon or two of petrol for the bike, and I'd been expecting Stan to see me right for the day. I counted my pennies and five p's – hang on, it wasn't that bad. I could afford a hot dog and one can of coke. I could pretend I'd eaten mine on the way back to the horse box.

So I bought the hot dog and the coke and walked back through the rows of vehicles. There were families eating off plates with knives and forks, and the grownups had glasses of wine! What would that girl think of me?

There she was sitting on the ramp, alone. I couldn't see Henry, and I didn't care much where he was.

'Er – they'd run out of burgers,' I said. 'Will this do?'

'That'll do fine! Honest, I can't eat much between events. You know, you're hungry and you can't eat.' But she bit the end off the hot dog and wolfed it. Then she asked, 'What about yours?'

'Couldn't wait,' I told her. 'I ate mine on the way back.'

'Liar!' she said through her mouthful. 'I saw you counting pennies. Here!' – and she stuffed the other end of the hot dog into my mouth. I felt my face going red, but when I'd taken a bite I had to smile and she smiled back at me.

I said, 'You know, like, I didn't have time to get to the bank this morning.'

'Me neither. Let's share this coke, I don't want a lot. All that gas won't get me over those jumps.'

'Not *more* jumps.'

'Show jumping this afternoon. But I'm not worried about that. All I need is a clear round. Henry can do it at a trot, I wish he would. And then!'

'Then what?'

'The cup! Touch wood, fingers crossed, things can go wrong. But with any luck we won't need the bank.'

A cup, eh! I had a picture of it in my mind, this great silver bucket, full of fifty-pound notes. She jumped up and fetched her Snoopy lunch bag and we shared crisps and biscuits and an apple, keeping the core for Henry.

'Oh well,' she said. 'Time to dress up again.' She nipped off to the little room and I wondered what she was going to look like this time. But it was back to the jacket, lumpier this time with the body-protector under it, plain black hat, and – spot the difference – brown gloves.

Henry was in Clare's horsebox and Clare's pony, Blaze, was between him and the ramp, so we had to untie Blaze and get her off, get Henry off, and get Blaze on again. Blaze didn't want to go on again, and we had to tug, push and smack her to get her up the ramp, and Trish began to look at her watch and get all tensed up again. But I helped Trish tack Henry up, and hoisted her into the saddle, and followed them to the show jumping ring. Perhaps you've seen the sort of thing on TV, all painted poles and fake brick walls and that, so I don't have to describe it. But – guess what? – I had to hold Henry again while Trish walked this course, and I could see now that it meant looking at each jump with a frown on your face and sussing out how not to knock it down. Henry and I were getting used to each other by now. I actually stroked his neck – one big smooth muscle.

'Keep you eyes on that cup, boy. Go for it!' I told him.

But I'd said the wrong thing again. Trish had come up behind us, calm enough.

'We're going to forget about that cup, aren't we, Henry? We're going to pretend we're practising in the paddock, and take it easy. We know you can do it.' Oh well, psychology, I suppose. But *squelch* for me.

I helped her up again. How many times had she got on and got off today? Her eyes looked distant. I wasn't there. They trotted off and went over a practice jump standing by itself. It looked easy enough.

A lady with a clip-board and a walkie-talkie called out, 'Number 33, you're next!' There was a P.A. going here, and a man's voice commentating.

'Entering the ring now is number 33, Patricia Niarchos-Jones on Kingsvale – er, Kingsvale Oboe.'

The nit! He'd got it all wrong! Somebody ought to tell him it was Trish and Henry. They might give the cup to the wrong person. He was over in that caravan, wasn't he? I made for it.

Halfway there, the penny dropped. More than one penny. Patricia = tricia = Trish. She had told me Kingsvale Haughtboys, not Oboe, but at least the first bit was right. And she'd never told me her family name, but I should have guessed it would be a posh double-barrelled one like Niarchos-Jones. What chance did I, Jeff Dooley, have with this Miss Patricia Niarchos-Jones, after feeding her half a hot dog? I remembered I'd got the motorbike with me. Why didn't I just ride off on it and leave her to it? This was her world, not mine.

Meanwhile I'd missed most of her show jumping. They seemed to be doing fine, Patricia steering to and fro among the coloured jumps jammed into the small ring, Oboe, or whoever he was, sailing over the poles with inches to spare, tucking up his back legs to make sure he didn't tip anything.

They were cantering up the side of the ring where I was standing when I saw this little dog. More like a spider than a dog, you know the sort I mean? Hair over its eyes so it can't see where it's going. It was trailing a red leather lead and it was going under the rope into the ring right in front of Henry! I don't think Trish ever saw it, she was looking out for the next jump. I threw myself down on my belly, caught

34

the lead, yanked the spider towards me and grabbed it.

But Henry had seen the dog. He made a little side-step at the canter, and Trish came out of the saddle, turned half a somersault and came down with a thump that shook the ground.

I shoved the little bitch into the hands of its owner who was glaring at me, and ducked under the rope. Trish was getting to her feet, white and shaken and with tears in her eyes, but still holding the reins. She saw me coming to help her.

'Don't touch me!' she gasped. 'Go away! Leave us alone!'

As if it was all my fault! Somehow she was scrambling back into the saddle.

'Patricia Niarchos-Jones has unfortunately had a fall, but is continuing her round,' said the smoothie announcer. I got out of the ring and watched as, with tears dripping down her set white face, she rode Henry over the last two jumps, then headed, sobbing, for the exit from the ring.

'I'm afraid that's thirty faults for Patricia Niarchos-Jones,' came the announcer's voice. But it wasn't fair! Henry hadn't refused or knocked anything down! It was that son-of-a-bitch dog's fault!

'Where's the ref?' I shouted to the clip-board lady. She pointed to the commentator's caravan. This time I ran all the way.

'Where's the ref?' I shouted again, poking my head into the caravan and looking for a little man with shorts and a whistle.

'I am the referee,' came the cold voice of a high-octane lady with a walkie-talkie.

'*Protest!*' I hollered. 'Number 33 was interfered with! By a dog!'

35

'What's this? What's this?' snapped the high-octane lady.

'A dog ran into the ring,' I said.

'I'll need witnesses,' she said coolly.

'There's me – and the lady with the clip-board, she must have seen.'

The ref lady worked her walkie-talkie. 'Priscilla! We have a protest here. Did a dog interfere with Number 33?'

'That's right,' came a voice in reply. 'I saw it happen. I'm trying to get another witness.'

'I'll take your word for it, Priscilla,' said the ref lady. 'And that of the gentleman we have here.'

She looked at me. 'Your name, sir?'

'Jeffrey Dooley,' I told her.

'Have you any particular relationship with the rider, sir?'

'Never seen her before today,' I told her. It was true but it felt like a lie.

'Thank you Mr Dooley, that's very public-spirited of you,' and she gave me a high-octane smile and turned to the announcer. 'We don't need a Royal Commission on this one, do we? I did wonder why she fell between jumps. Make a correction, please, Rodney. Clear round for number 33.'

I could have kissed the old battle-axe, but I turned back to the arena. There was a little screwed-up horsey type of man hanging around the door of the caravan and listening to what we said. He took me by the arm and pulled me aside.

'You're lucky to get that one on your side,' he whispered. 'Know what she is? That's a top Stye Perjury Magistrate, that is. Get yerself up in front of her, and she'll send you down or let you off in no time at all. Never no messin' around. You're right lucky.'

'Thanks for the warning,' I said, and ran back to find Trish. There she was, hunched miserably in the saddle, riding back towards the horse box. The correction came over the loudspeaker and a handful of spectators actually clapped. The commentator went on, 'May I remind owners to keep their dogs firmly on the lead.' But Trish didn't react. I caught up with her.

'Well done!' I said.

'I'm kicking myself,' she said wretchedly. 'I just fell off. It wasn't Henry's fault.'

'It doesn't matter, does it? You've got your clear round.'

She looked at me and I could see she was still dazed, 'No. Thirty faults. There goes that cup!'

'Didn't you *hear*? They've just corrected it. I told them it was the dog's fault.'

She shook her head in a doped sort of way and said, 'Dog?', and she wouldn't believe me until she had ridden to the referee's caravan and got it from the people there. And then she was laughing and crying at the same time, and somebody was saying to me, 'You will look after her, won't you?'

Actually her friends rallied round Trish the heroine and helped us see to Henry. Somebody's mum said, 'Trish, shouldn't you go and see the ambulance people?' but she shook her head and only winced a bit. And then it was time for the prize-giving.

Nothing very grand about it. The high-octane lady handed out ribbons, plus a few diddy silver cups you could stick a boiled egg in, to little girls who seemed really chuffed to get them. Wait for the real thing, I told myself.

'Fifteen hands and under, Challenge Cup, Patricia Niarchos-Jones.'

Trish marched up to the lady and was given a

brown paper envelope – and a cup the size of a small coke can.

'Well done, Patricia,' said the lady. 'That was a nasty fall. Are you sure you are all right now?'

Trish nodded, made a little grimace of pain, and walked back to me, smiling happily. She proudly showed me the coke can.

'Er, great!' I said. Well, I shouldn't have expected the FA cup or a snooker prize should I? 'What's in the envelope?'

'Dunno,' she said.

'Open it and see,' I told her. I hoped the cheque would make up for the cup.

She carefully tore open the envelope. And she pulled out a twenty pound note and a fiver.

'I've won *twenty-five pounds*!' she gasped, round-eyed.

I thought there'd been some mistake.

'Are you sure there's nothing else in the envelope?' I asked. She didn't even look.

'I've never won anything like this in my *life*!' she went on. 'It's a lot of prize money!'

The poor little rich girl! I reckoned she'd always had everything bought for her by her mum and dad, so she'd got no idea of money. I mean, I could earn twenty-five pounds in a Yarmouth hotel washing dishes if I thought it was worth it. I'd been looking forward to a celebration but that would hardly buy a bottle of champagne to spray around. At least I'd been reckoning to ask for fifty quid for services as driver and, well, hanger-on. But I couldn't even ask that.

The whole thing felt pretty flat to me as we walked back to the horse box. Yet Trish waved her envelope at friends standing by Range Rovers or luxury horse vans, and they said, '*Twenty-five pounds?* Well *done*, Trish!' It just didn't add up.

I'd been saying nothing much. But I had a look at the fuel gauge in the cab and I had to say it.

'We'll have to buy some diesel or we'll never get back.'

'Oh?' she said. 'Well, not to worry. This will be enough, won't it? But I'm saving up for a saddle so I hope there'll be some left over.'

So there we were, after a bit, sitting together in the cab, with Henry parcelled and tied in the back, heading back for Rushby. The traffic was heavy and it wasn't an adventure any more to drive that brute of a van. As soon as I could, I pulled into a petrol station and bought fourteen pounds seventy worth of diesel and one ice cream cornet. That would have to do instead of a champagne celebration.

'Didn't you want one?' she asked. I told her I'd have my hands full with all this traffic. She stuck the cone in her silver cup, and let me have a lick as we waited at the traffic lights.

'Can I ask you some questions?' I said.

'If they're not too personal,' she giggled. She seemed to have recovered. 'Anything you didn't understand about the events?'

'I didn't understand any of it,' I told her. 'Never will, I reckon. It's the personal questions that I want to ask. Like, when you fell off and I tried to help you, why did you say "*Don't touch me*"?'

'Oh, did I? I didn't know what I was saying. But there's a rule about jumping competitions, you mustn't get anyone to help you, or you're eliminated. Nothing personal, honest!' And she put her hand on my arm, which made me feel pretty good.

'OK then, what about that hug I got after the cross-country bit. Was that personal?'

'Don't suppose that was, either,' she laughed. 'It's what footballers do when they score, isn't it?' Her hand gave my arm a friendly squeeze, but then I was struggling in a crowded roundabout and she took it away.

So where was I? I was in the rush-hour traffic, coming out of Norwich. When I could take my eyes off the road to look at her she was peacefully asleep, sitting up in the cab. Like that, she looked about ten years old. How old *was* she? I hadn't got around to asking her that one.

When we got back to the stables there was a woman and some kids waiting. Trish introduced me to the woman, Joanna, but I didn't want to answer too many of *her* questions, so I pushed off on the motorbike. All I'd got out of that long day was a date with Trish, somewhere, sometime next week.

Funny, though – that was enough!

THE CONFIDENTIAL DIARY OF P. N-J

Saturday May 23 continued.

... so there I was on my knees in Henry's stable, doing up his travelling bandages actually, to protect his legs on the van – and praying for a driver! And suddenly here was this person flat on his face on the muckheap as if he'd fallen from heaven. I didn't really think of him as a person, just a driver. I mean why else should he be there? Strangers don't usually wander about Rushby at five o'clock in the morning.

When we were alone together in the cab I had time to notice he was hunky – sort of Stallion with Good Conformation. And I thought Look Out! But Ellie and Jennie and I could manage him between us, couldn't we? They're big girls. And then there was the awful news that Butch and Digger had got suspected strangles. Everyone knew there was a lot of the disease about. The whole show was nearly cancelled. E and J were quite right to tell me to keep away – but that left me to cope with The Hunk all by myself.

PAT TAKES TOSS – AND CUP !

Pat Jones had a fall from her pony Hobo at the Burlingham One Day Event. But the judges ruled that it wasn't her fault or Hobo's so she came away with the cup after all.

Trust the press to be there when you fall off and to get most of the names wrong. Nobody calls me Pat. However, *Fame at Last*, sort of – and all thanks to Jeff, driver, groom, hanger-on and fixer. Did I really thank him enough? What with no sleep, the bump and everything, I was so woozy at the end of the day I didn't know what I was saying. Did we make a date? Did I give him my telephone number?

Who and what is he?

Joanna says Monica's uncle did turn up, after Jeff and Henry and I had left, and of course he was peeved to find no horse box and no me. He told Joanna that before he gave up waiting a big cattle truck stopped in the road, then drove on when the people in it saw him.

Who and what?

3

Dead Cert

(Jeff's story)

I woke up with one thought in my head. I'd got to arrange a date with that girl Trish. No, there was another thought. I couldn't afford it. And I'd had this nasty dream.

I was sitting across the old beat-up armchair, doing nothing and not thinking much, when my mate Gary came in.

'There's an old banger out in the road with an old geezer in it. Says he's your grandpa.'

'If he says that he probably is,' I said. But I didn't move.

'What's up, Jeff?' asks Gary. 'You been moping about all day. Girls?'

'Didn't sleep well,' I told him. 'I had this dream. I wanted a new girl friend but I had five old ones to get rid of. Dreamt I had to chop their heads off on a chopping block.'

Gary stared at me. 'Look, mate, I'm not sure I want to sleep in the same room as a serial killer. And you're not Henry the Eighth so you'd never get away with it. Forget it!' Gary sometimes amazes me when he remembers things we learnt at school. Henry the Eighth! He had six wives, didn't he?

'What about that grandpa of yours?' Gary nagged.

'Tell him I'm coming, will you?'

I went to get my leather jacket. You know the times when you go through all your pockets, knowing there's no money in them but hoping for a miracle? I did that. There was a hole in one pocket, into the lining. I even poked my finger through that. A crisp bit of paper – off some packet of course. I got it out and it was a ten pound note. Miracle!

I felt all warm and happy. And then I suddenly went cold.

I remembered what that tenner was. Change for the diesel in Norwich on Saturday. It wasn't my money. It was the girl's.

Gary came in and looked at my face.

'He says he'll give you another three minutes – what's up now? Lost a pound and found a penny?'

'I found ten quid. But it's not mine.'

'Since when did that ever worry you?'

I got pretty mad at him. 'Look, there's money you can nick and money you can't. You don't short-change your girl-friend. What's she going to think of me?'

I heard a parp-parp from a motor-horn outside, and I stormed out. There was the neat little Fifties Morris Minor Traveller standing by the kerb, engine running, Grandpa at the wheel.

'Are you right, Jeff boy?' says Grandpa. 'Git in!'

I got in and said nothing. Grandpa worked the right indicator, stuck out his hand through the window, and drove off. Even that didn't make me smile as it usually did.

'Your mate there says you're frettin' about girls, Jeff,' says Grandpa. 'You're too young to be doing that. We'll go somewhere to take your mind off 'em, right?'

'Where are we going?' I grunted.

43

'Racing.'

I knew it. Just what I needed to take my mind off that horsey girl – more horses!

But to wind up Grandpa I said, '*Banger* racing?'

'You know what I think about banger racing,' he said. 'And if anything bangs in this car, that's your fault, not mine.'

I couldn't argue with that. We'd worked on that car together, as soon as I was too old for jigsaw puzzles. A little bit of this and a little bit of that, from different scrap yards. And – as far as he could make sure – all honest and above board. Some of the body-work *was* boards, a tidy job of carpentry and yacht varnish. If Grandpa couldn't find the right spare, he'd do wonders with a file, a vice and a micrometer. After he left the sea he had spent twenty years flat on his back under other people's motors and he knew exactly what he was doing, only needing me for help when his own rusty joints made the acrobatic bits difficult. I enjoyed working with him because he was the best teacher I ever had. He even let me help him on some really old vintage cars, for friends. But what good had all that done Grandpa? There he was with an old age pension and a Morris he could hardly afford to run. My dad, he had bigger ideas about buying and selling cars. Selling them, at least – he wasn't all that keen on buying. And where did they get *him*? Inside a place he can't get out of. Me, I believe in playing it clever.

Grandpa put out his hand again and turned carefully into Caister Road. A twenty-mile-an-hour tail-back built up behind us.

'When are you coming to live with me again, Jeff?' says Grandpa. I knew that question was coming up, and all.

'You know Auntie Shirl and me don't get on,' I

44

said. Of course he knew it. I was sorry for him, being looked after by Auntie Shirl. She'd got that job, looking after Grandpa, because she'd never married, never had it at all I suppose. Her ideas about sex made Grandpa look real cool.

But I could usually *talk* to Grandpa. And so I did. 'Gramps,' I said, 'suppose you've got some money, belonging to someone else, well she actually gave it you but she expected some of it back and you hung onto it just accidentally like . . .' It was more difficult to explain than I expected. We were at a red light so he was able to shoot me a stern glance.

'Are you in that sort of trouble, lad? Seems you've got to give it back and say you're sorry.'

I saw myself holding out a note to the girl, pressing it into her hand. It didn't look right. What might she think? I knew she wasn't the sort you could buy for ten pounds.

'I want her to – to think well of me, Gramps. I want to take her out.'

'Well, then!' he said, and the lights turned green and he drove on. We turned off into the racecourse car park and he backed carefully into a slot between a Volvo and a – what *was* it? A car I'd never seen. Long and low and sort of carved out of soap, know what I mean? I took a good look at it while Grandpa carefully put a Crooklock onto the steering wheel of his Morris and locked all the doors.

'Who's going to nick your old banger, Gramps?' I teased him.

'Who? One of them *collectors* that's who,' he grunted. 'That was my mistake. I thought I'd get myself a car that no one would look at twice, and now they tell me it's a *collector's piece*.' He spat.

At the turnstiles he paid my entrance like he always

45

does. He might be going to buy me a burger, too, but I know he'll never give me anything for betting.

We made our way through the crowd of racegoers to the information board. The three o'clock race was just off, and there was the usual quiet buzz from the Norfolk crowd. But I began to feel better. This scene sort of took away the taste of what had happened to me last Saturday. Over there, behind the rails, were the horses. All round me were the sort of people I was used to. Girls dressed to make you look at them – though somehow I didn't want to eye them today. There were older women with real good hair-dos. Coppers patrolling in pairs. And men who knew their business, counting their rolls of notes and stuffing them carefully into inside pockets. And I think I picked out one or two characters who would nick it out of those pockets if they could.

I took a look at the runners' board for the three thirty and . . .

Gobsmacked!

Number 5, Henry the Eighth, 7 to 1.

I'm not superstitious but . . . Yes everybody says that, I know. But, I mean, that was one hell of a coincidence, two horses called Henry. And dreams must mean *something* mustn't they? Everything was going to be all right.

Grandpa was muttering the name of a horse, Alley Barber or whatever. 'I can get better odds than that from Joe,' he said. 'Don't suppose you've got anything to put on, Jeff?'

I felt that tenner in my pocket. It couldn't be wrong to put it on my dream, could it? I'd walk out with seventy quid in my pocket, enough for a good evening out *and* give the girl her change back. No more problems!

'I'll come with you,' I said to Grandpa. We moved towards the bookie stands. Then I stopped.

There was someone ahead who I didn't want to meet.

'Here, put it on for me, Grandpa, will you?' I said quickly. 'Henry the Eighth. To win. Meet you at the paddock!'

And I pushed the tenner into his hand and turned round and made for the paddock where the crowd was thickest, waiting for the parade. I pushed though till I was up against the paddock rails. The three-thirty runners were led in. Number five? A *grey*! That settled it. When everything points in the same direction, you can't just take no notice, can you?

The push of the crowd was shoving me against a girl standing by the rails. She didn't seem to mind being shoved against and she turned her face and gave me a sort of come-on look, with a pair of rather bulgy grey-blue eyes. Usually – but no, today wasn't usual and I wasn't interested in pick-ups. But all the same, where had I seen that face before?

'Seen you before, haven't I?' I asked. I really wasn't interested in chatting her up, but you've got to say something.

'Not that I can remember,' she came back, playing haughty. Then I got it. It was the sour-faced girl I'd seen with Stan White. And not so sour as I'd thought. She'd put something on her face. Sugar?

'Royal Ascot, perhaps?' I said, sarcastic. 'The Queen's enclosure?'

She quite seemed to like that idea, and I could have followed it up, but there was some bad-tempered jostling behind me, and someone was breathing whisky fumes down the back of my neck. Two very heavy blokes wedged themselves one on each side of me along the rails, squeezing out the girl.

"Allo, Jeff boy! Good to see you're keeping in touch with the horses. Anything you fancy here?' the voice came from behind my ear. My heart sank. I knew Stan White's voice. I turned and pretended to be surprised. I didn't think it necessary to look too pleased, but I made a bit of conversation.

'Oh, hi, Mr White! Er – what do you think of Henry the Eighth?'

He and the two big men seemed to exchange little smiles.

'Yeah, Henery Eight. Very pretty horse, Jeff. Look, lad, about last Saturday.'

What was coming now? He could turn nasty, couldn't he? But *he* was the one who seemed embarrassed.

'We had this – er, this big council contract to finish, didn't we gents? So we had to call off the transport job. Another time, eh? We'll need your pertickalar experience. You and Charlene here could work together. You won't let us down, will you, boy?'

In front of that crowd he was talking *blah blah* like an important businessman. I felt like saying, in front of that crowd and all, *Bollocks, I saw you with your broken-down truck and you didn't see me*! What had I got to lose? I was finished with him. Wasn't I? But I didn't like the smell of those two heavy men each side of me – beer was what they smelt of. This wasn't the place to get shirty, so I just nodded.

'We'll be in touch then,' said Stan. And the three men and the girl moved away through the crowd.

What was all *that* about? Why did they bother with Jeff Dooley? Did Stan really think I was a horse expert? I suppose I might have laid it on a bit thick to him, some time, about what I did in Newmarket. Anyway, this had been some sort of threat. Like,

48

Stand by the gang! Don't think you can get loose from us!

Somehow they'd even shaken my dream. But it was more important than ever that the dream should work. If I broke with Stan that would be another source of cash gone.

The horses left the ring. Grandpa would have placed that bet by now, wouldn't he? The crowd thinned in the paddock as people made their way to the track. Of course I had to watch this race so I did the same. I felt sort of sick and anxious and empty inside, but I hadn't the price of a Polo mint on me. After the race, it would be different.

Wouldn't it?

The horses came trotting and cantering up to the start. There was Henry, the grey, pretty quiet. His rider – well, a lot less interesting than Trish, a really screwed-up jock, balanced up there on the stirrups. They all got into the starting bays without much fuss. And they were off.

That race really grabbed me in the pit of my belly. There was so much that was riding on it for me. Henry the Eighth seemed to be up with the leaders at the start. Then for a bit the runners were out of my sight. The commentator didn't seem to have much to say about Henry. He had to be a strong finisher, coming from the back, didn't he? The field came round the bend into sight again, a mass of coloured silks and black and brown horses. But there ought to be a white one!

From where I was I couldn't tell which horse was leading at the post. But I could see which one wasn't. The grey came in with the late finishers. As he cantered past me to the unsaddling place he looked quite fresh and his jockey seemed to be almost smiling – like those smiles on the faces of Stan's heavies.

I would have been sick on the spot, but luckily there was nothing in my belly. That was it, then. I couldn't stay in this place any longer. I made my way to the exit and the car park. Grandpa wouldn't be long, he never spun out his race meetings. Or I could just walk somewhere, like to the seashore, and jump off a cliff, only there aren't any cliffs at Caister-on-Sea.

So this was the end of the Trish story then. Her tenner had gone into the bookie's wallet and there was no prospect of any more cash. What was it I'd told myself? *You can't ignore the signs*. Not much doubt which way the signs pointed now! Out!

On my way to the exit I did look around for Stan and his followers. Perhaps I should have been a bit more friendly, I was going to need them, and the girl Charlene wasn't all that bad. But I couldn't see them.

I went to Grandpa's car. He wasn't there yet. I took a long look at the car parked alongside. The BMW badge on the front. On the back a row of figures and letters, 5L V12 GT. *Five litres*! But the coachwork and the windows were dirty, and seagulls had been using it as a bombing target. Even weirder, the rubbish piled up underneath: dead leaves and newspapers, plastic beer glasses. A live pussycat! That car had been there for some time.

So where was the owner? An Arab horse-breeder who'd flown home and forgotten it? A rich jockey in hospital with a broken neck? A punter who'd lost his shirt and couldn't even pay the petrol?

'You're a beauty,' I murmured to the car, 'and you've got no-one to love you!' I'd given up horses, again. Perhaps I would give up girls too, and stick to cars. Standing casually alongside Grandpa's Morris, I tried the door of the BMW. Gently. I didn't want to set off a lot of alarms. Locked.

50

'Hands off, young man!' I tried to hide a guilty start. It was only Grandpa coming up behind me, looking stern enough, but he wouldn't shop me.

'How often have I told you not to touch!' said Grandpa, making me feel like a toddler in Tesco's. I wouldn't take that sort of telling off from anyone but Grandpa. 'And look here, young Jeff!' he went on. 'I saw you talking with Stan White, didn't I? You keep clear of that man, I tell you! Or else!'

I shrugged. 'Else what? You keep telling me to look for jobs. I was trying to keep clear and he comes and *offers* me jobs. What am I supposed to do?'

'You know well enough what I mean. Git in!'

He unlocked the Morris and we got in. Before we did up our seat belts he reached into a pocket and held out a handful of notes.

'That's yours,' he said, and pulled out the choke.

I stared at the notes and didn't take them.

'But he lost!' I said.

'Who lost?'

'Henry the Eighth lost.'

'Of course he did, you young fool. What did you expect of a horse like that?'

'I dreamt he was going to win!' I said.

'Did you really?' he said, sarcastic.

I thought a bit. 'No I didn't. I dreamt I *was* Henry the Eighth. Not that, either. Gary *said* that's what I dreamt. Still, dreams and names must mean *something* mustn't they!'

'That horse lived up to its name all right,' Grandpa cackled. 'Seven horses in front of him at the finish, and Henry the eighth! So ain't it lucky I didn't back him for you? I couldn't do that, not to me own grandson. I put your money on Ali Baba, dead cert at five to one, and here's your fifty.'

Grandpa sat back in the driver's seat, without even

51

starting the engine. 'It's like what I've always told you about motors, Jeff boy. Nothing to do with magic nor dreams. You've got your fuel, you've got your compression, you've got your spark – it's got to go. With horses, now, you've got your form, you've got your jockey, you've got the right going. So?'

'You've got your winner?'

'Don't you believe it,' he chuckled. 'Anything can happen! It makes a change, and I reckon that's why I go racing – where are you off to, Jeff?'

I had taken the money and opened the car door again.

'Just seen a telephone box. Can you change this for the phone? Thanks a lot, Gramps!'

'Don't you go and spend that on too many women, now!' he called out to me.

'Right!' I called back. 'I promise! Not more than one at a time!'

And I knew which one it had to be.

THE CONFIDENTIAL DIARY OF P. N-J

Monday May 24th

Now be reasonable, Patricia Niarchos-Jones! You've had your little adventure, your alien encounter. Let him go back to his Unknown Planet, and forget about him! Haven't you got enough on your plate with revision and farm accounts and darling Henry? Anyway, why do you think he should be interested in meeting you again? He can't have had much *fun* on Saturday, holding Henry, not understanding what was going on, not knowing anybody. And I can't have impressed him much, falling flat on my back (ouch!)

52

right in front of him. I must have looked pretty silly. *Forget it!*

All the same, he's the Handsome Stallion! And I owe that cup to his help.

He's phoned!!! – to confirm a date he says we made. I dithered, though I hope it didn't show. Tried to be nice to him, but I went on about previous social engagements (liar!) and said I'll ring him back. What shall I do? Got to talk about it with somebody. What about Chantal? Doesn't she lead this Sex Life in raving old Norwich?

I rang Chantal. It went something like this:

Me: Chantal? Look, I want to talk to you about something.
Chantal: Trish? Hi! Sorry, I don't know anything about horses.
Me: No, this is serious!
Chantal: I thought you were only serious about horses.
Me: Oh shut up, Shanny! I've met this boy—
Chantal: However did that happen?
Me: He fell from the sky, of course.
Chantal: He'd have to. There's no other way to get to Rushby, is there? Is he a parachutist?
Me: I don't know what he is but he wants a date with me.
Chantal: Great! I'm really pleased for you, Trish. So what's the problem?
Me: I don't know what else he wants.
Chantal: Just sex. That's what they all want. No use waiting for the Big Romantic Deal, Trish, ring on your finger and roses round the door!

Me: Maybe that's what I *am* waiting for.
Chantal: And cornflakes for breakfast together?
           Forget it, Trish! If it's my advice you're
           asking, Trish *dear*, you could do with a bit
           of casual sex. With people. Or you'll get
           real kinky, like all the other horsey girls.

There was quite a lot more like this and it was
beginning to put me off the whole thing, like somebody telling you spinach is good for you.

But I *like* spinach. She could be right about the
kinkiness, couldn't she?

I'll ring Jeff back!

4

Joyrides

(Jeff's story)

'Meet me at the church,' I said to Trish over the telephone.

'Oh, Sir, this is so sudden!' she giggled. It sounded like a quote from some old book. 'Have you told the vicar and the bellringers?'

'Look, the church is a good place to meet because we both know where it is,' I said. And because nobody ever goes there, I could have added, and because I didn't want all the village to see me and the car. I'd gone to a lot of trouble over this car. Of course I wanted to impress Miss Patricia Niarchos-Jones. I had even stopped carefully in a lay-by to make this call on the car phone, because – well, to be honest I wasn't all that sure how to work either the phone or the car.

By the time I reached Rushby I'd got used to the car, the only trouble being that it kept doing eighty before I'd noticed the speed. So I got to the church quite a bit earlier than I'd calculated and she wasn't there. I hate waiting. I began wondering again. Were we both talking about the same church? Did she think I meant half past six tomorrow morning? Why should she want to come out with me at all? And how many more passing drivers were going to notice a BMW 5 litre V12 GT parked by the churchyard? Well, at least I had the quadrophonic CD player to listen to, with its autochanger in the boot.

There she was! My heart gave a bump as she rode up on her rusty little pushbike. Her blonde hair looked shampooed, floating loose and long in the breeze, and she was wearing a black-and-white top with a print of a rearing stallion on it. A teensy little bit of makeup! She looked almost sophisticated. But her eyes popped wide open when they saw the car. Which was what I had hoped for.

'Hi!' I said. 'Good to see you! Would you like to lock up your bike in the churchyard?'

She wrinkled her nose. 'I'll just dump it. Nobody's going to nick this old thing.' She could say that again. But when you own a horse worth a few grand, who cares what your bicycle looks like?

She dumped it behind a bush and came back staring at the BMW.

'Nice car,' she said.

'Glad you like it,' I said. 'I chose it specially for you.'

She sat in the soft leather passenger seat – there was only room for one passenger really. I pressed the buttons so that she could see over the dashboard better, and she giggled as the angles and the headrest adjusted themselves. 'Hey! A massage machine. Just what I need!'

'How are the bruises?' I remembered to ask.

'OK. But I wish I had an easy chair like this at home.'

I put on my seat belt and turned the ignition key.

'*Will the passenger please fasten the seat belt?*'

'All right, all right, you don't have to talk like a flight hostess!' she said, her green eyes flashing at me. Not a good start.

'I never said a word,' I told her. I'd have to watch this car. Here was I trying to say the right things, and the car had to put its word in. 'That was the voice synthesizer,' I explained.

'Ah. We could do with one on the old horsebox.' She put on a synthesizer voice: *'The passenger is strangling itself with its haynet.'*

I'd hoped we would talk about something other than horses today, but I laughed at her joke. I switched off the music. I couldn't hear if the engine was running or not.

'Why have you turned that off?' she said. 'I was enjoying it.'

I turned the music on again. Some fuddyduddy stuff like the Beach Boys. But then the owner of this car would have to be middle-aged. I kicked the automatic transmission and we glided smoothly forward.

'Where are we going?' Trish asked casually.

'You said you wanted to see the Golden Mile.'

'Do you want to?'

'Me? I've seen it,' I told her. 'If you live in Great Yarmouth it's not where you go. But I'd like to take you there.'

She paid me with a smile. On a corner of the lane I jammed on the brakes. A farm tractor-and-trailer was coming the other way. The peasant who was driving it seemed to expect me to reverse. The tractor had a lot of big spikes aimed at me and I wasn't going to argue. Where was reverse? I managed to back into a field entrance and the rusty machine scraped past.

We came out of the lanes onto the A road and turned right.

'Isn't Yarmouth the other way?' she asked.

'Yes, I know,' I said. 'But this animal needs some exercise.'

57

She seemed to understand that. The longer way round took us onto some faster roads, some of them dualled. I could have done with a real motorway, an autobahn like they have the other side of the North Sea, or something like Silverstone. I had read up about this car. It had an electronically limited top speed of 155mph, but I would settle for that.

As I played carve-ups with an angry red Sierra on the Beccles bypass I watched Trish out of the corner of my eye. She was sitting back, relaxed and dreamy. I might have preferred it if she'd been gripping the side of the seat and screwing up her eyes, like some passengers I'd had. Was she just ignorant? Didn't she *notice* the bursts of acceleration? Still, I'm not a hotter. I haven't smashed anything up yet – I *like* cars too much. And as long as she was happy beside me!

We had to crawl through traffic round Lowestoft, and there was time to talk. I thought I'd get my words in first.

'Can I ask you some more questions? You went to sleep in the cab on Saturday.'

'Yes, sorry, I was very tired.'

There were lots of things I wanted to know about her, but lots of questions I didn't yet dare to ask. I stuck to the regular ones.

'Do you like discos?'

'Yes.'

'Which ones do you go to?'

'Last disco I went to was the Beccles and Bungay Riding Club one.'

'Oho! Sirs in red coats drinking champagne out of hunting horns, eh?'

'Not quite,' she said coolly. 'Little kids and coke cans.'

Was she sophisticated or wasn't she? It was important to know. I tried again.

'What's your favourite group?'

'Rhesus Positive,' she said immediately. And she'd scored again. I'd never heard of them but I wasn't going to admit it.

'Yeah,' I said. 'They're OK. Did you watch that show on the telly last night—'

'No,' she said.

'Hang about!' The traffic was thicker and I was trying not to get rattled. 'I haven't said which show yet.'

'I was watching one of the ponies with colic last night.'

That must be better than watching paint dry, but I didn't say it. Now for the crunch question. I made it casual.

'Got a regular boy friend?'

'Of course.'

'What's his name?'

'You know it.'

'How can I know it? Oh, don't tell me, let me guess. It's Henry.' And she giggled.

'Can I ask you a question?' she said.

'Ask away,' I said, but I wasn't as happy as I tried to look. Was it going to be *What happened to that tenner*?

'Is this your car?' she asked. That was the easier one and I was ready for it.

'Oh no, it's a company car.' It sounded good and it was almost certainly true. You'd be a twit to pay for a car like this out of your own pocket, something like sixty grand.

We were clear of Lowestoft, and then there were some dualled bits towards Great Yarmouth. Stupid Escorts overtaking slowly in the fast lane! I found the switch and flashed my lights behind them. I did notice Trish stealing a glance at the speedometer, but I think

59

she read the rev counter and it didn't mean much to her.

We passed a road sign and she suddenly said, 'What's great about Great Yarmouth?'

That was quite a good conversation starter.

'Great Yarmouth, birthplace of Jeffrey Dooley, of course,' I told her. 'Can't think of much else. It's great for OAPs and for families from Wales, stay in one of them little boarding-houses and get ripped off along the front. We used to have scooter gangs coming in, thousands of them, and that woke the old place up a bit. They've cleaned that up now. But we'll go in the docks way. That's sort of real.'

We drove over the Haven bridge and you could see it was high water. A dozen big offshore vessels, oil rig tenders, towered over the quaysides, with names like CECILIE VIKING and TOISA PANTHER.

'That's where the power is,' I said. 'My grandad used to go to sea in a steam trawler. They called him the donkeyman. But each one of them tender's got a pair of seven thousand brake-horsepower diesel engines.'

'Cor!' Trish gasped. 'Fourteen thousand horses on one boat!'

'Why did I have to mention horsepower?' I groaned. 'It's really naff, measuring all that power by what a pony can pull.'

'I like it,' she smiled. 'Look! That big ship's unloading treetrunks. Lots of crosscountry jumps!'

'You're encourageable!' I said. I knew as I said it that I'd got the word wrong.

'Encourage me, then!' she said with a grin.

'I'll take you for the rides on Pleasure Beach.'

'Sounds great! Should I have worn my jods?'

Along past Norfolk Line Carriers and the Birdseye

factory, round the corner where the sand blows over the road and –

'Ooo!' she went. 'The sea!'

'It's usually there,' I told her coolly. Same old North Sea I'd known all my life. And yet, with Trish being all enthusiastic beside me, perhaps it looked more sparkly today.

'I didn't bring my swim things,' she said, disappointed.

'You wouldn't want to swim in that,' I told her. 'I'll buy you a bucket and spade.' Was I being too nasty?

'Promise?'

'I promise.' Girls are for teasing, but I wasn't sure yet who was teasing who.

There was a bit of a breeze and the waves were breaking on the offshore sandbank.

'White horses!' she said. It was getting to be a game, bringing in horses where there was no call for them.

I drove on to the entrance to Pleasure Beach and parked the car in the central parking area, locking the doors. There was a little stall selling things for the beach. Trish nudged me with her elbow. I couldn't ignore that nudge, it seemed to have an electric current running through it.

'You promised,' she said, pointing to plastic buckets and spades. Feeling a right wimp, I went and bought her one of each, the cheapest, in dayglo colours. And then I saw something else and had one of my brilliant ideas. Little china piggy-banks! I bought one of those, too. This was the way to get over my big worry.

I gave her the bucket and spade. Then in front of her eyes I pushed a ten pound note into the china pig.

'Didn't you say you were saving up for a saddle or

61

something?' I said with a smile. 'I kept this note of yours until I could find you something to save it in,' and I handed her the pig.

Her eyes went wide in real puzzlement.

'What do you mean, my note?'

'Change from the diesel we bought in Norwich on Saturday.'

'No, there can't have been any change, Jeff! I know what a fill of diesel costs for that van.'

I needn't have worried at all! But I told her I hadn't filled up, and she thought it was ever so sweet of me to think of the piggy-bank.

'And it's a saddleback piggy too! You *are* thoughtful, Jeff!'

So there we were, all friends, and set up for the evening on the Golden Mile.

I led her to the Pleasure Beach entrance. The usual family parties and gangs of teenyboppers were crowding in and crowding out, and from the rollercoaster came the usual screams.

'You've got to scream, dear, or you'll end up laughing.' A couple of old biddies staggered off cackling with laughter at their joke.

BOTTON'S PLEASURE BEACH, the bright lights said. ENTRANCE FREE.

'So what are we queueing for,' Trish asked.

'To change our money. We can't spend pennies here.'

'It's OK. I don't need to yet. It's like being abroad, isn't it?'

'That's right,' I said. I *have* been to Benidorm. 'All the thrills of foreign travel. Welcome to the Costa Bloata! Four *bottoms* to the pound sterling.' I bought a £5 bag of them and told her to have a look round and choose a ride.

Why did we have to pass the Tots' Korner first?

There was a diddy little roundabout with, yes, horses on it. It had stopped.

'That one!' she said. 'Coming with me?'

But I was paralysed by something I'd seen. Oh, no! Not now! Not here! I knew that flaming mop of red hair – Zandra, ex-girl-friend, coming this way, between two hulking foreign sailors.

'Hold my bucket and spade, then,' Trish said, and climbed into the saddle of a wooden horse. Zandra was taking in the scene with cool delight.

'Hi, Jeff!' she cooed with her loud stage voice. '*Baby*-minding?' And walked on.

The bitch! Oh, I knew at that moment that I was really through with her. I didn't care what she thought of me, but how could she insult my poor little Trish?

Trish heard all right. She sat haughtily on her dappled steed, looked down her nose, and spoke up in a loud county sort of voice.

'Who's that *mature* lady, Jeff? Your auntie?'

Something at the back of Zandra's neck told me that she'd heard, too. And I knew something else – that poor little Trish could look after herself.

She had her horsie-ride and then she let me take her on the big stuff. We got aboard the Looping Star, and its multi-g centrifugal forces threw our bodies one against the other as it was designed to do, and the sea and the sky spun around us and she laughed and screamed as she was supposed to. I let her take me on the dodgem cars and sat with my arm round her waist as she fought with the crude steering and bumped her way round. She had belly muscles like steel ropes, I suppose you get them from riding. Then she fancied the Giant Slide. You climbed high above the crowds and inserted yourself into one of the kinky tubes that slope down to ground level. The kinkiest part was that the red tube and the green tube spiral

63

round each other, and she insisted that I got into the red one and she got into the green one and we both started together, so we would go side by side and under and over each other all the way down. But in fact it was lonely inside that tube and I didn't like it all that much.

We kept the biggest one till last, the rollercoaster. Trish was enjoying herself all right, on a high as she'd been at the end of that crosscountry course. Me? Well, I'd done an off-season job maintaining that rollercoaster once. It makes you think of the things that can go wrong. I knew it wasn't such a good piece of engineering as the BMW. Still, for most of the ride we each spared an arm to put round the other one, high up there above the illuminations and the crawling traffic on the front.

We creaked slowly up to the highest point, and Trish pointed downwards.

'Look, Jeff – oops! *Wheeee!*' The rush down the steepest slope took the words out of her mouth and left them behind.

During the slower bit along the bottom I asked her what she'd been going to say.

'Oh, nothing, just that I saw another car just like ours – like *yours* – driving along the front. *Ooff!*'

A wicked bit of acceleration round a curve winded her again. But the nasty feeling in my guts now was nothing to do with the ride. I'd never ever seen a car like that coupé anywhere else. It wasn't likely there'd be another one in Great Yarmouth. Unless Trish was mistaken, something had gone seriously wrong with our evening.

As soon as the ride was over I directed Trish, bright-eyed and protesting, towards the exit. We both looked towards the slot where I had parked the car. The slot was empty.

64

'It's gone!' Trish exclaimed. 'Look, there's a police-man standing where you put it. Go and tell him it's been nicked!'

On no. That policeman was waiting for the person who had parked the car. Person unknown, with any luck. Was the cop strolling, too casually, in my direc-tion? I had to get Trish out of there.

My next move was another brilliant one. At the side of the road was the rank of those grotty old horse-drawn carriages that plod up and down the Golden Mile.

'Come on,' I said. 'I got another treat for you!' And I grabbed her by the arm, pulled her into the first carriage, and lay back on the seat.

Her eyes lit up again. 'Oh, Jeff, I *wanted* to do this. How did you guess? But the *car?*'

The car? My mind was still whirling, trying to think what to say.

'It's all right,' I yammered. 'My mate must have collected it. Company driver, he is. I expect they need it.'

'Ten pounds to the other end of the mile, *sir*. All right?' It was the driver speaking.

'Home, James, and don't spare the horses,' I said, cowering down on the cushions. Where had I heard that bit of nonsense? Some prehistoric song.

'That's what everyone say,' growled the driver. 'An' I only got the one old mare. Time she 'ave 'er supper.'

'Ten pounds a mile, Jeff? Is that all right?' Trish queried.

'Thass the *golden* mile, mam, don' you forget! A bit special to remember on your 'oneymoon. Get on, Booty!' The old horse began to move forward.

'Poor old Booty!' Trish said. 'We're not in a hurry, are we Jeff?'

Clop, clop, clop, clop, clop. The old horse broke

into a trot. We were safe enough. Cops don't look for hotters in horse-buggies. Yet I could have cried for the ruin of our beautiful evening.

But what was happening? Here was this girl snuggling up beside me, and her fingers running through my hair.

'Relax, Jeff,' she was saying. 'Easy! Easy! You're all tensed up.'

Clop, clop, clop, clop, clop. I'm not good at relaxing, but there was something about that *clop clop clop* that slowed you right down. The illuminated lamp-posts passed slowly overhead, and above them a star showed in the evening sky. On our right the moon was rising over the Krazy Golf course. On the left passed the ever-switching coloured lights of *The Flamingo, Golden Nugget, Silver Slipper, The Mint* and *Caesar's Bingo.*

'Don't you want to play the video alleys?' I asked feebly.

'No, Jeff, I like it like this,' she murmured.

I liked it too. Our fingers were interlaced, I felt her warm body alongside mine, and she smelled of nice things like shampoo, with only a trace of stable, and that may have been the old carriage – but what was happening to it?

'Easy! Easy!' – and it wasn't Trish's soft voice but the carriage-driver shouting anxiously. We both sat up. The old horse was prancing about in front of the carriage, trying to go backwards, squealing with fright.

'It's that motor-bike, Jeff!' Trish said urgently. 'We've got to do something. Just tell them to keep quiet and stay still!' In a flash she had opened the door, jumped out, and run to the horse's head. She took hold of the bridle.

'All right, girl!' Trish was crooning. 'All right, Booty. Stand! Stand! Steady there, old girl!'

There was this motorbike at the intersection, trying to emerge onto the seafront. Ten grand worth of red-and-white Yamaha bike with two sets of matching leathers, boots, gloves and helmets, one of them riding pillion. Yes, they looked really great, like something from another galaxy.

'Look, mate,' I shouted to the goon who was gunning the engine. 'Do you think you could just sort of switch off and keep still?'

He didn't blast me with a nuclear-fusion pistol, but did what I asked, and lifted up his visor.

'Sorry, squire,' he said. Quite a nice bloke really.

'The old horse thought you were out to get her,' I said.

'Thought she was going to get us!' he grinned. I could see why he was worried. All that gear was brand new, honeymoon stuff. I went up to help Trish who was gently trying to get the horse off the pavement.

'Hang on to Booty,' Trish told me. 'The rein's tangled.' I hung on. Then – wouldn't you know it? – up strolled the inevitable copper. He had his eye on the colourful bikers, but he spoke to me.

'What's the trouble, sir?' There must be something about horses that makes policemen respect you.

'It's all right, officer,' I said. 'Nobody's fault. No harm done.' I can do the English Gent stuff if I have to.

'Quiet as a lamb she is, mostways,' the worried driver was saying.

The policeman strolled on. Trish and I got back into the carriage.

'You'll be all right now, miss,' said the driver. 'Quiet as a lamb, you see!'

We went on at a walk past Magic City. At the Leisureland Pool Room there seemed to be what they call a Police Presence and I was glad we hadn't gone there.

'Where can I set you down, sir?' the driver asked.

We were alongside all the restaurants. 'This will do,' I said. I helped Trish down and felt for the wallet in my pocket. Did I have enough left for this drive *and* a meal?

The driver waved me away. 'You don't owe me nuffen. You two kids really got me out of a heap o' trouble. I could a' lorst me licence, but for you. Good luck to you.' And he drove off, *clop, clop, clop, clop* . . .

'Wasn't that nice of him?' Trish said. 'I'm sure he looks after Booty.'

'Come on,' I said, 'let's eat. I want to make up for that half hot dog.'

There were half a dozen restaurants crowded together on this bit of the front, and their placards saying COD'N'CHIPS and CHILDREN'S POR-TIONS overflowed onto the steps and into the street. I didn't want to hang about outside so I took Trish straight into the nearest one.

Posher than I'd thought – should I be wearing a jacket and a tie? No, there were blokes no more dressed up than me, eating cod'n'chips too. A young waiter came up to us. He *was* wearing a jacket, a red one, and black bow tie, and he looked foreign.

'Have you reserved, sir?' Oh no, not one of those places! It did look full except for some tables with *Reserved* on them. A bigger and fatter waiter loomed up. The look on his face seemed to say *What have we here?* I remembered I was still holding that ridiculous bucket and spade.

'Can I help you, sir?'

68

Help us out the back way so the fuzz won't see us.
No, I didn't say it out loud. It was Trish who piped
up, with her best smile.

'Kalispera! Ena trapezi ya thio atoma, parakalo.'
Eh? Was that really her making those noises?
Whatever they meant they seemed to work. Big
waiter and little waiter were now all smiles and jab-
bering back at Trish, and conducting us to a table in
a little alcove with plastic leaves. They held our chairs
for us and handed us menus covered with squashy
red leather. I opened mine – and I couldn't believe it.
It wasn't only that a lot of words didn't make sense.
Half the actual letters weren't real letters either! But
Trish had her nose in hers and seemed to be busy
choosing and ordering.

'Taramasalata ... htapothi krasato ... lahano
dolmathes ... ke ena kilo Zeroalco. Oh, Jeff, how
clever of you to find this place! But what are you
having?'

'Er – I'll have the same as you.'
'You don't have to,' Trish said.
'It's OK, I like that sort of stuff,' I told her. The
waiter smiled and went away, and came back almost
immediately. With bread and water.

You want to be careful before you let yourself in
for a meal in this sort of place. There you are, face
to face with the girl, and there's nothing to do but
talk. There was some kind of tinkly muzak going on,
but not nearly loud enough to drown a conversation.
I looked into those green eyes, above a candle which
the waiter had lit on the table, and they laughed at
me. It was time I took control again. I came the heavy.

'Well, Miss Patricia Narko-Jones—'
That shook her a bit. 'How did you find out my
name? I never told you – oh, of course, at the show.
Anyway it's Niarchos-Jones.'

69

'What's the Niarchos bit?'

'My dad. He's in the Merchant Navy.'

Owns a fleet of tankers, I thought. But I didn't want to be told that.

'What were you going to say, Mr Jeffrey Dooley?'

'I just like to know what's going on. What's all this parlay-voo, French, Spanish, Italian or whatever? It's all Greek to me.'

'That's right.'

'What is?'

'It's Greek to me too. It's the Greek Merchant Navy that my dad's in. I thought that was why you brought me here.'

I'd kicked another own goal. I should have left her feeling impressed, and not shown my ignorance.

'Glad you like the place, anyway,' I said a bit feebly.

'Are you sure we can afford it, Jeff?' I did like the way she said *we*.

'Sure. I made it to the bank this time. With a gun!'

Trish looked a tiny bit scared at my joke about the gun, but I didn't mind that. She ought to be scared, going out with a guy like me. But then she laughed.

'So we won't have to do the washing-up?'

Wouldn't be the first time, if it came to that. That was another of the things I didn't say aloud.

A waiter brought a big wine bottle, wrapped in a serviette. I couldn't see all the label, but I could see the name ZEROALCO. It sounded fierce. He poured me some in my glass, and waited for me to taste it. I'd seen guys do this on telly commercials.

'Hmmm. One of these deceptively strong ones, I'd say.'

The waiter, po-faced, poured two glasses. We clinked them over the candle.

'Patricia!'

'Jeffrey!'

70

All was going well again – so long as we could think of things to talk about. She cleared her throat.

'Ahem. Do you live in Great Yarmouth?' she asked politely.

'Yes.'

'Whereabouts?'

'Oh, I live in a hotel.' And why should I tell lies? Some people might put an 's' in that hotel, but it certainly had been a hotel once.

'Sounds grand,' she said.

'The food's not all that grand.'

'So what are the beds like?' she asked, and then – it was like disco lights changing – she suddenly turned a pretty shade of pink when she heard herself say 'beds'. I'm sure she hadn't meant anything, and it was a bit early in the evening for me to make anything of it either. And anyway the waiter arrived with food. He saved me having to give that answer to her question: *The beds are hard narrow iron ones, in dormitories.*

Under my nose there was a bowl of something that looked like strawberry ice cream and smelt strongly of fish. Trish ate hers with bits of hard toast. I ate my toast.

I didn't want her to question me any more about my hotel, so I asked her, 'Where do you live, then?'

'Rushby Manor Farm.'

But of course. The manor. Where else? What could I say to that? I took a swig of Zeroalco and tried to eat some fish ice cream.

'Don't you like your taramasalata?'

'I – er, prefer it a bit less salty.' I thought that was rather neat. Tactful, you know. After all, she'd chosen it.

'It's the way they make it on Mykonos,' she said.

'You ought to be on the telly,' I told her. 'Do a food show.'

'I'd rather do a horse show.'

That made me laugh. 'We had five minutes' talk without horses. Not bad!'

She laughed too. 'Er – let's choose something else to talk about. You don't want to talk about horses. I don't want to know about cars. We can't seem to talk about our homes and families. So let's talk about *us*. And let's try and tell the real truth. Right?'

'Right. Who's going to start?'

'People say that first impressions – *really* first impressions – are what matter. Let's talk about first impressions. When I first saw you—'

'I was flat on my face in the muck. And you laughed at me.'

'No,' she said carefully. 'I didn't laugh at *you*. I laughed at Monica's uncle falling about. Then I saw a handsome young stranger instead, and asked if you were all right. I really cared. What did you think of me?'

'I heard you laugh. I don't like being laughed at and I should have been mad at you. But I thought, *that's a nice laugh*. Then I saw your face over the stable door and I just thought *nice face*.'

'So it wasn't such a bad start. Well, then I was glad there was someone to drive the van.'

'And I thought you were the girl I'd been told I would meet so I let you organise things. I thought you were very tough and efficient, until you cried.'

'You were very kind and patient, helping me at the show.'

'Kind and patient? But I'm not that sort of guy!'

'OK, you don't have to admit it. Do you know what really grabbed me? You felt for the horses.'

'How do you know?'

'You asked whether they like having girths round their bellies and bits in their mouths.'

'Well, do they?'

'Nobody ever asks. I've never heard a man worrying about that. Or a woman for that matter. It showed you were sensitive.'

'*Sensitive*. Me?' I wasn't sure I liked this line of talk, but I said nothing. Then she asked, 'Why did you ask me out this evening?'

I thought a bit more and said, 'To impress you.'

'Why not impress somebody else?'

'Umm . . . Because, since I met you, I hadn't been thinking about anyone else.'

'I thought a lot about you, too.'

Meanwhile the waiter had cleared away my half-eaten bowl of tarara salad or whatever it was and brought us another course. Rubbery little washers that didn't taste of anything much. Trish seemed to be enjoying hers and I chewed a few without thinking.

'So here we are,' I said. 'Talking across this table. We've known each other for one and a half days. That's not much to talk about, is it?'

'You could say what you feel about me now. This instant. And honest. No chatting up.'

'Oof! It's hard going, talking to you!'

'That's honest enough to start with!' she laughed. 'Don't you enjoy it?'

I chewed on an elastic band. 'Ummm . . .'

'You're not allowed to stop and think!' she said sharply.

'I dunno if I'm enjoying it or not. It's like this food. It's *different*. Do you always talk to people like this?'

'Oh no. With most people I know exactly what they're going to say, and I don't even listen, and neither do they. It *is* different with you, Jeff.'

'We like each other because we're different?'

'Could be. Wait a minute. Does that mean different from other people, or different from each other?' she asked.

'Are we different from each other?'

'I'm a girl and you're a boy.'

'I'd noticed that,' I told her. 'I'm thinking about it all the time. That's one reason we're here, isn't it?'

'Oh yes. If you'd been a girl I don't suppose I would have wanted to take a lift in that car and go on those Pleasure Beach rides and everything—'

'You did want to, with me?'

'Of course!'

'You're not allowed to say *of course*. That's chatting-up language. Did you really want to come with me?'

'Ummm . . .' Her turn to stop and think.

'Yes or no?' I insisted.

'Half no and half yes. And the yes won.'

'Why?'

'I suppose I'm a positive person.'

'Not because you liked me?'

'Oh yes, the fifty per cent was liking you.'

'What about the other fifty per cent? Since we're being honest.'

'Well, you seemed to be a city slicker. You like cars, and to me they're just things for getting from A to B. And I just didn't know anything else about you.'

'You were afraid of what your mum and dad would think?'

'We're talking about *us*, not parents! What didn't you like about me?'

'Have I got to say?'

'Yes.'

'I thought I liked big girls and you're a shorty. You were bossy and you smelt of horse shit.'

She gave a sort of whoop of laughter. 'I asked for

74

that! Yet you asked me out tonight, and not one of your other girl friends. I bet you've got lots, living in a place like Yarmouth.'

'We're not talking about other girl friends. We're talking about us, and about this evening.'

'Then tell me why you were so uptight when the girl said you were baby-minding? That was this evening, remember?'

I sighed. 'OK. That was Zandra, my girlfriend—'

'Oh, sorry, I shouldn't have been rude to her. She's sort of beautiful.'

'My ex-girlfriend. She's sort of beautiful, and sort of an actress – at least she did a drama course, and she's sort of a bitch. She left me for a sailor when my cash ran out. Ah, I didn't have to tell you that.'

'Did you – did you have a lot of sex with her.'

'Not this evening, I didn't.'

The waiter was hovering, and removing Trish's empty plate. He looked at mine.

'Do you not like the *htapothi*, sir?'

'What exactly is it?' I asked Trish.

'Oc-to-pus,' said the helpful waiter.

I felt sick. 'He's joking, isn't he?' I appealed hopefully to Trish.

'No, in Greece they eat octopus like in England we eat chips,' said Trish. 'Are you feeling all right, Jeff?'

I stood up, unsteadily.

'I need a bit of fresh air,' I said. 'Look, I told you I'd drive you here and drive you home. I'm going to find another car.'

She grabbed me by the arm and made me sit down.

'No, Jeff, no! I'll get myself home. There's a late bus. I checked. I always check on the late buses.'

'Don't you trust me?'

'Not with cars, I don't. I don't know how you got

75

that posh car, and I don't want to know. I don't want you to do that sort of thing for me.'

'Are you chicken?'

'Yes, if you like, I'm chicken.' I thought of her belting over those cross-country jumps. She could afford to cry chicken. She went on, 'If you want to do something for me, you can *stop* doing whatever it is that you are doing. Get it?'

'I still need fresh air,' I said.

'Let's go on the beach then.'

So she helped me settle the bill and tip the waiter, and we walked out arm in arm under the twinkling lights of the sea-front, and I breathed the petrol fumes, smells of cooking, and sea air. She asked how I felt.

'Better, thanks. Must have been that wine. Deceptively strong. What was it called?'

'Zero-alcohol. That's why I chose it. Come on, we're going to play sandcastles.'

I was feeling much, much better. Sandcastles with Trish on the moonlit beach wasn't at all a bad idea. We jumped down the sea-wall, landed in the sand, and raced each other towards the sound of the breakers.

'I won!' she laughed.

Of course I had to let her. She sat down in the dampish sand.

And began to make sandcastles!

I sat myself beside her, put my arm round her shoulders, and pulled her quite gently towards me. Her body was warm, but hard and resisting. She was tough, but I knew I was stronger than her. I put my hand up under the jumper with the rampant stallion and felt bare flesh. I tried to pull the jumper off over her head.

'Oh, don't tear it!' she said angrily. 'Let me do it.'

76

She jumped to her feet, and with a few quick movements peeled all her clothes off. I stood up and started to do the same. As I kicked off my jeans, she ran down the sloping beach, splashed a few paces in the shallows, dived into an approaching wave, and disappeared.

I stood there, naked and chilled. I can swim, but I don't like the sea much. I know the North Sea too well, it's got currents and undertows and it never seems to get far above freezing. Brass monkeys don't bathe in it, most of the year. But I waded in after her. There was no knowing what crazy thing she might get up to.

'Trish!' I called. A breaking wave filled my mouth with salt water. But there was her head, like one of those seals you sometimes see. I swam towards her, gasping as the cold froze my eyebrows. As for the lower parts of me, they had ceased to exist. We met, standing in the waves. I ran my hands all over her hard flesh, like an ice-cold marble statue, and just as exciting. My body had totally forgotten what it had wanted to do to her. Our lips met, in a salty, fishy kiss. *Taramasalata.*

'Look out!' she cried. A mountainous freak wave reared up darkly behind me and bowled me over. I heard her laughing, and then I was struggling to find my feet in a black swirl of water, sand, seaweed, and other nasty things that float around. Where was up, and where was down? I didn't have time to ask where Trish was.

Sand and stones grazed my shoulder. I got my hands on the bottom and then my feet. As I stood up I felt the backwash of the big wave trying to carry me out to sea, and I had to lean against it hard. I spat and coughed up salt water and wiped it from my eyes, as I staggered towards dry land. But where

77

was little Trish? Had that undertow carried her off? I stared around and thought I was going blind. I couldn't even see the moon any more. I could see the whiteness of the waves as they broke on the shore, then a blackness of water then, out on the offshore sand bank, more white breakers. Her white horses! She hadn't been crazy enough to swim out and join them, had she?

She could still be under the black water, crushed by that freak wave. I turned back into the sea and desperately felt around with hands and feet where I thought I'd last seen her, hoping and not hoping to touch that smooth body. Above the water, my eyes could see very little. As I plunged below it, I saw nothing at all. It was hopeless! All by myself, I couldn't search the whole North Sea. I stood up in the shallows and called into the darkness with all the voice I could find.

'*Trish!*'

Her name was drowned by the hissing of the breakers. Was she drowned too?

As I stood there calling, the sea and the shore were lit up again as the moon came out from behind a thick cloud. I looked again for a sign of her sleek seal head above the water, but there was nothing to break the shining path of moonlight on the sea.

Why would nobody *help* me?

Because you haven't called for help, Jeffrey Dooley. Because you'd do anything rather than go to the cops.

I had to get some clothes on first. I ran out of the water but I couldn't see the clothes anywhere. Of course, the tide carries you along the beach, but which way? I was swearing and sort of sobbing as I ran down the beach, saw that I'd gone too far, turned round and ran up the other way, calling her name now towards the land as well.

My foot struck something in the sand and I swore again. Some fool of a kid had left its toys there. No! Trish's bucket and spade! Oh, why hadn't I let her play with her sandcastles? She was only a kid!

And there were my clothes, half buried in the sand, not how I'd left them. I pulled them on anyhow.

But where were *her* clothes?

I searched around, even digging with that hateful plastic spade, but there was no sign of the jumper with the horse on it, nor bra, pants, jeans or sandals.

Someone had nicked all her clothes, and tried to bury mine? It didn't make sense, but I had no time to think about it.

The moon lit up the stretch of damp sand, left smooth by the evening ebb tide. There were the tracks of our running feet, coming from the promenade. There were the marks of our bums where we'd sat, and the signs of a bit of a struggle. There were the tracks of her running into the sea, and of me walking after her. There was the track of me coming back from down the beach just now . . .

Yes, and of small feet doing the same! And there, all by itself, was a line of little running footprints, leading away up the beach towards the Wellington Pier.

I looked towards the lit-up Golden Mile, still crowded with evening strollers. No use searching there for someone who doesn't want to be found, if that was where she'd gone. But I followed the track towards the pier. Nothing to prove it was hers, any girl could have made it.

After a bit the footprints seemed to slow to a walk, and so did I. There were words written neatly in the sand.

LOVE, NOT RAPE!

THE CONFIDENTIAL DIARY OF P. N-J

Thursday May 28th

Reminder: *ASSINGATION*. No. *ASSIGNATION!*
Meet Jeff at Rushby church 6.30 pm. (Why the
church? What have I let myself in for?)
   I didn't mean to drown you, Jeff!
   Now steady, Trish, girl! No use getting hysterical.
Tell yourself he walked out of that sea and went home
and will never want to speak to you again. (Writing
this the morning after, as usual.)
   My *telephone's* ringing. I don't want to answer it.
The mortuary? The coast guard? The police? Jeff
himself?
   Of course I had to lift the receiver – and guess
who? Chantal of all people. I suppose I'd asked for
her kindly interest. It went something like this.

Chantal:	Trish? Well? How did it go?
Me:	How did what go?
Chantal:	You know. Your date? Did he pick you up?
Me:	Yes, in a BMW 5 Litre V12 GT.
Chantal:	(Quite a long silence) So, your new boy-friend must be *loaded!*
Me:	He'd nicked it.
Chantal:	Ha ha! You're joking?
Me:	I don't feel like joking, Chantal.
Chantal:	Trish, it sounds like you had a ball!
Me:	Oh yes. We drove to Othello's in a one-horse landau, and dined there.
Chantal:	You're not kidding?
Me:	I'm not telling the half of it. Like evading the cops.
Chantal:	And?

80

Me:	And what?
Chantal:	Tell me the big climax!
Me:	Sandcastles on the beach.
Chantal:	What do you mean, sandcastles?
Me:	You know, you dig up the sand with your spade and put it in the bucket and—
Chantal:	I know how to make sandcastles, twit! What *else* happened?
Me:	A bit of attempted rape.
Chantal:	Aha! Only attempted?
Me:	Yes, I chose to have a swim instead.
Chantal:	Oh God, Trish, I might have known you'd blow it! You had the chance of a roll on the beach but you went for a freezing swim, so you *must* be kinky. But what happened then?
Me:	I think he got drowned and I left him for dead. And I caught the late bus home, full of drunks, and I picked up my bicycle in the churchyard, and I was thinking It's OK, God, I have Defended My Virtue. But, oh, Shanny, there was this full moon overhead and I pedalled home thinking of that bit of Shakespeare we did, you know, *to live a barren sister all your life, chanting faint hymns to the cold fruitless moon* . . .

I had to hang up there because I was making myself cry, but I *was* feeling better for that talk with Shanny, and it's helped to write it down too.

I think I'll go for a ride on Henry.

5
CHAUFFEUR!

(Jeff's story)

In his hard iron hostel bed my mate Gary opened one bleary eye.

'For chrissake wassa matter, Jeff, got ants in your bed?'

I was sitting on my own bed putting on my trainers.

'Sand,' I said. 'I don't feel sleepy.'

'Other people do,' he groaned. ''Specially when you keep them awake all night screaming.'

'I wasn't screaming,' I said. 'Was I?'

Gary opened another angry eye. 'You was sort of trying to scream, strangled like. And shouting that the octopus was going to get you.'

The nightmare came back to me and I wished it hadn't.

'No,' I said. 'The octopus was getting her, not me.'

'Oh oh! Might have known there was a girl in it. Zandra I s'pose?'

'No. This other one. And she *fed* me on octopus.'

'You mean you dreamt you ate an *octopus*?'

'No, I really did. Last night.'

Gary was wide awake now, and he settled himself on his pillow with a sigh. 'Come on then. Tell Gary. I won't get no peace till you do.'

So I told him what had happened last night. Apart

82

from Grandpa, Gary's the only person I tell things to. He doesn't interrupt much.

'So you treat this girl in a posh restaurant and she makes you eat yuk and tries to drown you?'

'She ate the same, and she swam like a fish. What d'you think I ought to do, Gary?'

'If this is all true and you didn't dream it, my advice is ditch her, Jeff mate! Chuck her back in the water. They say there's more fish in the sea. Why are you tying your trainers?'

'Going to the beach. Got to make sure I didn't dream it.'

Gary turned over and groaned, and I left him. He called after me something like 'Is the string tied?' I couldn't think why he was fussing about my string shoelaces so I ignored it.

Sam the warden saw me go. 'Jogging, Jeff?' he asked, a bit surprised. He approves of us doing body-building and that but I don't go for early morning jogs much. This time my two legs couldn't carry me fast enough. I just had to get to the beach and check up. Had I read those tracks on the sand correctly? I wasn't a Red Indian tracker, was I? Perhaps somebody else had made all those marks on the beach. I ran down Regent Street, onto the front, and jumped down from the sea wall to the sand. A chilly wind blew off the sea, which was the colour of a tarmac road, with a lot of little white waves. White horses. Oh God! Where was she now?

The sand at the top of the beach was dry, and had been trampled by hundreds of footprints. Nearer the sea it stretched flat and damp. Lines of seabirds were standing there, looking out at the horizon. Some of them took off as a man came running with his dog. I wanted to shout at him, *Get off! You're spoiling her tracks!*

The Wellington Pier was on my left. I had seen her footprints leading towards it, hadn't I? But now, apart from the tracks of the man and his dog, and the arrow-head footmarks of birds, there was nothing at all. Not even the tracks my own feet had made last night. Had I really dreamt it all?

What did you expect, thicko Jeff Dooley? The high spring tide in the night had come and gone, and swept away the whole record. I wished that time, like the tide, could come and go like that, and erase the whole track of everything that had happened.

No I didn't. I had to find Trish and make sure she was still alive. I went back and sat on the chilly sea wall, and collected my thoughts. *All simple enough. You blew it. She gave you the slip and took the late bus home. You could check up on that with a phone call.*

Not so simple. I'd had trouble with those other phone calls, getting on to people who didn't want to know me, before I'd eventually got on to her. No, I had to see her, face to face. So I had to go to Rushby.

I ran back to the hostel. Of course I'd missed breakfast, but that was the least of my worries. Gary was doing chores.

'I didn't think about the tide,' I said to him.

'But I *told* you it was spring tide!' he said. Oh, yes, so he had, he hadn't been on about bootlaces. But anyway the run had cleared my head and I knew what I had to do.

I put on my leather jacket and boots.

'Here, Gary,' I said. 'Do us a favour, mate. Smuggle my helmet out with the trash.'

He took the plastic bag from me.

'You want me to bin it?' he asked doubtfully.

'Course not, nit! I just don't want Sam to get suspicious. I'm going for a ride. Tell Sam, I'm – I'm after a job I've heard about.'

Gary just went 'Huh!' as if no one would believe that story. I slipped outside without Sam noticing and took the helmet from Gary by the bins.

'Have fun!' he wished me, pretty envious.

Now for the motorbike. Like the other things I drive from time to time, it was an underexercised vehicle, or it would be if it wasn't for me. There are lots of empty houses in a seaside town like Yarmouth, and I'd noticed this bike standing in a shed alongside one of them. Nobody ever seemed to come to this house, not even at weekends. The owners must have been in jail or something. I got sorry for this bike. I was able to spend a little time fitting a proper key to it, and I made sure it had enough oil, and air in the tyres, and I took it for little walkies. I was doing it a favour, wasn't I? And I always brought it back and cleaned it up and locked it up safe from thieves.

So there it was this morning, waiting for me. I waved cheerfully at the neighbours. I'd been walking in and out of that yard for so long that they knew I was all right. I took the cover off the bike, wheeled it out, and we were off.

I felt happier now I was on the go, weaving in and out of the town traffic, then speeding along the country roads, but not overdoing anything. The winding road across Haddiscoe marshes, all left and right bends, was as good as the Looping Star at Pleasure Beach. *Oops?* Had I missed a turning? Wasn't that the place that isn't a post office?

Never mind, we'll take the next lane on the right, and circle round.

Fatal! Just shows what a townie I am, doesn't it? Once you start circling round these Norfolk lanes you can go round and round until you drop and leave

85

your bones for the rabbits to gnaw. I got to know those rabbits quite well, individually. They leapt out to scare me as I passed, then they sat at the side of the road and laughed as I came around for the second and third time. There were these signposts, the sort you can't read till you've gone past them, all of them saying either RUSHBY, or RUSHBY MARSHES or BY ROAD. Not a peasant in the fields to tell me the way.

Yet suddenly there it was. A big entrance labelled RUSHBY MANOR. I stopped and put my feet to the ground.

I looked at the winding drive, and the house which I could just see between trees. And I almost turned round and went back to Yarmouth.

I knew what would happen if I drove along that drive. I'd have to walk up countless steps to a big front door and bang the old brass knocker – no, pull the old fashioned bell-pull. The door would be opened by a butler who would look down his nose at me and say . . .

Say what? *Miss Patricia asked me to say . . . 'Get Lost?' Miss Patricia was regrettably drowned last night?*

What was the use, going on? Yet what was the use, turning back?

I burned up that drive and came to a skid stop on the gravel. I killed the engine, put down the stand and took off my helmet. Not many steps up to that front door, and the house itself was smaller than I expected. Quite a lot of windows though. One of them must be – my heart revved – *her* bedroom.

There was a plain electric bell-push by the door. I went up and pushed it. Perhaps she would come to the door herself and . . .

Nothing happened. I pushed the button again. Nothing happened. For a long time.

It was pretty quiet there, apart from the noises of different sorts of birds. Yet there was one little sound I kept hearing, behind me. *Snip, snip, snip-snip, snip* . . .

It was coming from the garden. I don't know anything about gardens, but I guessed that most of what I was looking at was weeds. Yet perhaps somebody was working there. *Snip, snip-snip*. I followed the sound.

I came round some rose trees – I do know roses – and there she was. Trish's mother? Trish's *grand*mother? Really old, anyway.

She gave a start, and started talking. What she said went on for quite a long time.

'Oh, good morning! You gave me quite a fright! A little bit deaf, you see, so I didn't hear you coming. Though I did seem to hear a motor, now I come to think of it. Did you have difficulty finding the place? Everybody does. You do look young, I must say. But then, when you come to my age, everyone looks young. Especially policemen! I don't know what you young people want nowadays. You don't seem to know what you do want. I really thought any man would fall in love with her! I've talked to so many of you, and now it seemed that people had stopped coming, but here you are, eh? So young! But I think you look honest. I can usually tell, you know. I suppose you'd like to see her first. They all like to see her, but I don't know, perhaps she's a bit old fashioned, and takes a bit of living up to. Come along then!'

I didn't know what to say, but it didn't matter, because she didn't give me the chance to say anything. It felt like a dream, but if it was, it was better than dreaming of octopuses. She carried on talking as we walked along a weedy path and came out on the gravel drive. She saw the motorbike.

'Oh! What's that thing doing there? Of course, it must be yours. It looks well cared for. Some old people don't like these *bikers*, but I'll tell you a secret. I was one myself, for a time! During the war. World War Two of course. *And* I had to do all the maintenance. I know you wouldn't believe it to look at me now. Snipping a few rose heads is about all I can manage.'

We were moving towards some outbuildings at the back of the house.

'She's in the stables, as you might expect, just waiting for you, eh? Oh, by the way, I can let you have a bed. But you're not thinking of getting married are you? In my day, young men didn't bother their heads with thoughts of marriage, they just got stuck in on the job . . .'

I couldn't believe what my ears seemed to be hearing. Perhaps I was getting it all wrong. But all I cared was that she was leading me to Trish. And it sounded as if I was expected!

'Perhaps you'd like to open the big doors?'

I undid the big doors and swung one open. The old girl managed the other one, and said, 'There she is!'

There she was. Not Patricia.

But if anything could have made up for the disappointment, it was what I saw. The silvery radiator and black coachwork of a beautiful old Bentley. The number plate said simply JOY 2.

'There!' the old lady went on. 'Isn't she a beauty? Aren't you in love with her already? Oh, I can see that you care!' A bird had left a splotch on the bonnet and I was gently trying to remove it with spit and a bit of tissue. 'Now then, let me take a look at you. Yes, I do believe the uniform would fit you very well. And of course you'd like to see the chauffeur's flat. It's up the wooden stairs there. I won't come with you, I don't like stairs, but do have a nose round by yourself. The uniform will be hanging in the wardrobe. Come and knock on the back door of the house when you've had a look. Take your time.'

She wandered off towards the house. Still in a dream I went up the wooden stairs. A pad, warm under the stable roof. A sofa and armchairs, not new of course, and a little kitchenette. A sink, a tap, a black-and-white check teacloth hung up to dry. Through another door, a bedroom with just room for a single bed and a wardrobe. I opened the wardrobe. It smelt of mothballs. Hanging in it was a black jacket and breeches, and on a shelf above I saw a black cap with a peak, plus a sort of World War One crash helmet. There was a spotty mirror on the wall. I took off my leather jacket and jeans, and put on the breeches, jacket and cap. They fitted well enough. I glared at my reflection in the glass. Only one thing missing. I went to the little kitchen, reached down the black-and-white teacloth, folded it and wrapped it round the headpiece of the cap.

'Might I see your driving licence, please, *sir*!'

There you go, P.C. Dooley!

I went down to the old car. I opened the side flap of the bonnet and looked at the engine. A beautiful museum piece. I recognized the twin carburettors and the magneto. I could manage those – none of your send-it-back-to-the-factory computerized units. I would clear out the cobwebs later. I closed it up and went and sat in the driver's seat. A rather stiff set of levers adjusted the seat. In the glove compartment was – guess what – a pair of black leather gloves. I put them on and practised saluting. I tried the heavy clutch, gear lever and brake. I could cope.

So I walked across the yard to the back door of the house, in full uniform. I knocked, hard, remembering the old lady was deaf, and I heard her call, 'Come in!' A passage led to the kitchen, and she was in there talking to a cat. Then she was talking to me again.

'Oh, *yes!* It does fit you, doesn't it, nearly? I think you're a *little* slimmer than Eustace was, so perhaps you'd like to take it away and get it taken in here and there. I'm sure your tailor would do it for you, or your mother or somebody. Now, you'd like a cup of coffee, wouldn't you? A biscuit?' I nodded, the only way to get a word in edgeways. 'There you are. Yes, please sit down. Just because it's the Manor we don't have to stand on ceremony these days, do we? Now, what was it I had to tell you about? Oh, yes, *references*. I'm sure you're a thoroughly honest and respectable person but my son insists that I take up references on these occasions. He's a lawyer, you know. In New Zealand. He keeps saying I ought to go and live there with him but, I don't know, it is such a long way from anywhere, isn't it? You'll have no difficulty in producing three references, will you? Oh dear, those biscuits went very quickly. Perhaps you'd like something more substantial. There's probably something in the fridge. Do you understand fridges? This is such a noisy old thing, you'll find the Bentley very much quieter. Yes, you're in luck. A pork pie? Just a minute, I'll find you a knife and fork. There. Now, what else? Oh yes, money. My bank manager says I can't afford to pay you more than seventy five pounds a week. He says that's not very much these days, and I have to take his word for it, but then there's the free living quarters and electricity

90

and – er, the garden produce. So that's agreed then? I'm sure we shall get on together like a house on fire. Start as soon as you can. Is there anything you'd like to *ask* me?'

Phew! Get it in quick. The one important question, blow the rest!

'Can I see Patricia, please?'

'Eh? I told you I'm a little deaf. I thought you said Patricia.'

'Yes,' I said loudly. 'Patricia. I'd like to see her.'

'You did say Patricia? I'm afraid I can't help you there, young man. I assure you there's nobody of that name here. I don't know anyone called Patricia. Well it's been *so* nice chatting to you. *Good*bye. And you'll let me have those letters as soon as you can?'

She held out her bony hand for me to shake, as if we were sealing a bargain. I suppose I should have saluted, but I stumbled out of that kitchen into the yard, and round to the bike in the drive, with my head in a whirl. I put the chauffeur's cap in the carrier box, put on my black-and-white helmet, started the bike and drove off. I rode down the drive, and it wasn't until I was out in the lane that I began to think clearly.

I had been talked into a job that I hadn't even asked for. It had seemed almost too good to be true, and the prospect of living in the same place as Trish had made it perfect. But Trish didn't live there.

I didn't think the old lady was hiding anything from me. She'd been so casual and offhand when she said she didn't know a Patricia that it had to be true.

It's an old trick, Jeff boy. The girl had given me a false address. I wanted to gun that bike along those lanes to work off my rage and confusion. But there was an animal ahead of me. A horse with a rider. In the old days I would have bombed past them, just for a lark, but I understood horses now. It might have been someone like Trish and Henry, mightn't it? I slowed down behind them. The rider turned round to wave me on.

It was Trish and Henry.

I rode slowly up beside them. Trish steered Henry in towards the left-hand bank and waved me past. But I had to talk to her so I chugged along at Henry's walking pace. Henry didn't like the bike alongside him and started dancing and prancing and rolling his eyes.

'Will you *please* go past, you're frightening my horse!' Trish's voice didn't sound at all friendly. I went on to where there was a wide opening into a field, switched off the engine, took off my helmet, and waited for them. Trish rode up, surprise on her face.

'Jeff! I thought you were a policeman!'

'Do you usually yell at policemen?'

'Yes, if they frighten my pony. And I was worried. I thought a policeman had come to say – to tell me you were drowned.'

So she did care! She'd been as worried as I had. I could make *her* feel guilty.

'I might have drowned, for all you cared. And why did you lie to me about where you live?'

'What? Oh, we can't talk here. Henry's fidgeting. Look, I'll go back to the stables over the fields. We'll meet there, all right?'

'Where *are* the stables?'

She pointed over the fields with her whip. 'There, by those trees. Keep going left. See you!'

And she and Henry were off at a smooth gallop. Was she eager to meet me, or had she given me the slip again? But I kept going left and, yes, there was the church, and the two farms, and the stable yard. I left the bike at the entrance and walked in. A tiny little kid goggled at me.

'Where's Trish?' I asked him.

'Tackwoom.' He pointed to the end of the row of stalls, then ran off. 'Nan!' I heard him squeaking. 'Pleeceman!'

Henry put his head over his half door as I passed, his ears laid back. I recognized Nelson too, looking quite friendly. I looked into the open door at the end, and saw the back view of Trish, straining to put a saddle on a high sort of bracket. She turned, and smiled, not quite sure of herself.

'Hello, Jeff. Er – take a seat. Push that cat and those brushes off that stool.'

There wasn't much room to spare in the tackroom. There were about a dozen saddles on brackets round the walls, and bridles hanging underneath them, and plastic boxes full of brushes and tools on the floor, and piles of rugs and a bucket full of whips, and boots and hats everywhere. It smelt of leather and polish and horse dung.

'A Spit?' she offered, holding out a can of drink. I took it, and she opened one for herself.

'Cheers!' we said together. It was cosy and relaxed in that tackroom.

'I was worried when that wave knocked you over,' she began straight away. 'And you were under for quite a long time, but I saw you stand up. Then for some reason you went back into the sea, and you went the other way down the beach, and I left you to it. I'm so glad you're all right.'

'You might have said goodnight.'

'Yes, sorry, but I was still mad at you.'

'*You* were mad at *me!* When a girl invites a guy down onto the sands in the moonlight, what's a guy supposed to expect?'

'Sandcastles and skinny-dipping,' she grinned. 'Or whatever *she's* in the mood for. I was mad at you for being so *clumsy*. Did you read my message?'

'I got the message. I thought that was finish, between us. But this morning I had to know for sure. Why did you give me the wrong address?'

'I didn't!' she replied indignantly.

'You did. I went there and they'd never heard of you.'

'Went where?'

'Rushby Manor.'

She put her hand over her mouth. Was she hiding a grin or a gasp? 'You didn't go *there?*'

'That's where you said you lived.'

'I'm sure I didn't. I'm sure I said Manor Farm.'

'Is that a different place?'

'It certainly is. Did you see the old lady?'

'Yes. We got on all right.'

'But she's crazy!'

'She's no more crazy than I am.'

'That could be true. So you got on with each other. Two crazies together! What did she say to you?'

'A lot. I can't remember it all.'

'And what did you say to her?'

I counted on my fingers. 'Five words, I think. "Please can I see Patricia?" And she said she didn't know you.'

'She doesn't know me. It must have been tough for you!'

'It came out all right.' I thought for a bit. 'Trish, can you give me a reference?' She gawped at me. 'You know, a letter saying I'm hardworking and honest.'

'But you're not hardworking and honest.'

'I know, I just need someone to say I am. I need this job. There's this beautiful old Bentley. And a bedroom.'

She looked at me half seriously, half mocking. 'Jeff, I'm sure it's your idea of heaven. But what would you *do* with yourself, stuck out there at the Manor?'

'I could see you. Manor Farm's not far, is it?'

'I'm busy with the horses all the time. You're bored with horses.'

'You could teach me to ride.'

Her eyes lit up with all sorts of mischief. What had I said, so thoughtlessly?

'*Right!*' she said. 'Would you like to start now?' She jumped to her feet. 'Hats? Hats? You can't ride without a hat, it's a rule of the establishment.' She gathered up an armful of tatty riding hats and plonked them on my head one after the other. 'Bighead! None of them fit. What are we going to do about a hat?'

'I have a perfectly good motor-cycle helmet,' I said with dignity – then I wished I hadn't. I'd lost my cop-out.

She exploded with a puff of laughter. 'You can't ride in that! Hang on – why not? You'll look great! Now then, boots?' She looked at my feet. 'They'll do, if we can find stirrup-irons big enough. And Nelson's been groomed and he really needs the exercise.'

A nasty feeling was growing in the pit of my stomach. She sounded as if she meant it.

'Look,' I said. 'There's no hurry, is there? We could make a date. I've got business to attend to—'

'Liar! Come on, it's now or never. No riding lesson: no reference. Go and get your helmet – and no skiving off!'

Would I want to skive off? Yes. But now she'd said it, I couldn't. I walked off and fetched my helmet, dreading what was to come. *Me*, on a horse? And of all horses, my old friend Nelson who'd dragged me in the dirt!

By the time I'd got back with my helmet on, Nelson was standing there saddled and bridled. He tossed his head and snorted and sniffed at my helmet, but Trish told him sternly to stop fooling around.

'Make friends with him, Jeff. Give him a pat.'

I tentatively patted his neck and he turned his head round and used me as a scratching post. Quite friendly, though. I looked up at the saddle. It seemed a long way above the ground. How was I supposed to get up there?

'I'll lead him to the block,' said Trish. The block? That's what they used to chop people's heads off on, wasn't it? I knew how they felt, those wives of Henry the Eighth!

The block was a set of solid steps at the end of the yard. Trish led Nelson up to it. I climbed up the steps. There was the saddle alongside me, as unsteady as a boat alongside a jetty. Leg over! And there I was, with this huge *animal* between my thighs. Trish pushed two leather reins into my trembling fingers – and Nelson's head immediately plunged down out of sight before me, very nearly dragging me off before I'd even begun.

'Don't let him put his head down!' Trish told me. As if I could do anything about it. She shoved my feet into the stirrups on each side, and said, 'Walk on, Nelson!'

It had been bad enough, standing still. You know, a motorbike's designed for a man to sit on. A horse isn't. I once tried to ride one of those old penny-farthing bicycles. You're dangerously high above the ground with nothing in front of you. Must have been designed by a horseman, the feeling is the same. And now the whole thing was moving, not smoothly like a machine but swaying from side to side and lurching forward and back. I forgave all those riders I'd accused of being toffy-nosed and snooty to people on the ground. They're really scared stiff of falling off, *all the time*.

And Nelson was only walking. Not fast. The scenery was hardly changing as the minutes dragged past. Trish was leading him by the bridle into the exercise paddock. As she opened the gate, she let go.

'Don't let him go!' I snapped.

'He's all right, aren't you, Nelson?' Perhaps he was. I wasn't. He put his head down to grab a mouthful of grass. This time I was clever enough to let the reins out. He raised his head and walked through the gate. There was nothing to prevent him breaking my leg against the gate post, but he didn't.

'Shorten your reins, Jeff,' Trish said. How do you make a rein shorter? Which end do you start? She gathered them up and put them back into my hands. In the exercise paddock there were all those jumps painted red and white.

'I'm not going over those things!' I said, getting my voice back. Trish laughed.

'I'll give you two or three years before we do the jumps.'

Somehow those words got up my nose. *Three years!* What sort of wimp did she take me for? I'd learned to drive a car in weeks. But I was behaving like a wimp, wasn't I?

'You can let go, now,' I told Trish. She smiled up approvingly, and stood back. Nelson plodded very slowly round the track of woodchips.

'Relax, Jeff!' she called. 'And kick him on!'

If I relaxed, I'd fall off. If I kicked him he'd probably kick me back. But something was improving, it was hard to say what. I was letting the bottom half of my body move with the sway and the lurch, instead of fighting it all screwed up. I was even getting a bit bored with the very slow progress. I tried a kick.

Those bikers' boots are pretty heavy and no-one likes being kicked in the belly with them. Nelson reacted. What was happening? Instead of the swaying walk, there was this beast underneath me bouncing along like a bike jolting across sleepers on a railway line. I had tried that once, not for long, and the bike saddle had more springs than this one. I hadn't reckoned on this heavy massage between the thighs, and I thought each jolt would be my last before I'd be bumped off onto the ground many feet below.

'Well, *done*, Jeff! Trot on, Nelson!'

So this was trotting? It felt like an earthquake.

'Where are the brakes?' I gasped as I passed Trish the second time.

'Do you want to stop? Pull him up firmly with the reins. That's what they're there for.'

I pulled. Nelson walked. I kept pulling and he stood still.

'Let him have his head,' Trish said.

'He's welcome to it.'

'Slacken the reins, I mean. Don't let them go altogether! We'll do some exercises. Touch your left toe with your right hand. Now your right toe with your left hand. Now go round the world: take your feet out of the stirrups, put your right leg over the same side as the left. Yes, you can! Now put your left leg over the other side so you're sitting back to front.'

'Are you taking the mickey?' I protested, looking down at Nelson's bum. 'I don't want to join a circus!'

'They made me do all these things when I was three,' she said.

'Give me the adult version,' I told her. 'Can I sit properly now?'

She made me do some more daft exercises, such as

98

circling my arm like a windmill while Nelson walked. I was determined that she wouldn't get me to fall off, and I didn't. And, yes, I was getting used to being up there.

'That'll do for now,' she said, opening the gate. 'Ride him back to the stables.'

I steered him back and made him stop in the yard. Trish wouldn't let me get off at the block.

'Feet out, right leg over and slide!' she said.

My feet hit the ground. My legs could hardly hold me up. Muscles ached which I didn't know I had. Nelson nearly knocked me over, rubbing his head on me. I gave him a friendly slap.

'OK, thanks, *teacher!*' I said. 'Tell me I'm hopeless.'

'You should have started eighteen years ago,' she said.

'Don't be daft,' I told her. 'I wasn't born—'

'Ah ha, just what I thought!' she sang.

I realized I'd told her my age, and tried to cover up. 'I wasn't born yesterday, I was going to say.'

'You'll learn, Jeff,' she said. 'You'll learn.'

THE CONFIDENTIAL DIARY OF P. N-J

Thursday June 7th

So where was the press photographer when I had Jeff arse-about-face on Nelson, dressed in biker's gear?

I've got to admit I'd been a bit afraid of Jeff the Hunk up to that moment. But once a girl's made a fool of a bloke he can't scare her any longer. And, seriously, he's got to be sort of mature if he can take being made a fool of. I've decided he's really rather a sweetie!

6

The Pad

(Jeff's Story)

Trish and I woke up in that chauffeur's pad.

What? I'm missing out the interesting bits?

But it's my affair, isn't it, what I tell and what I don't tell? And that bit was between me and Trish, wasn't it?

No? You really need to know what happened?

OK then, if you must know. It was good, I can tell you that. I just hope I can find good enough words for it.

That evening we had walked across the fields together, from the stables to the Manor. Walked? Well, for one thing I wasn't too keen to sit on another saddle, not even that comfortable motorcycle one. I though I'd give my bum a rest. And Trish thought the bike would make too much noise.

It was a warm summer evening. There was a sunset. Birds were flying across it. Trish said they were gulls, and they always flew back towards Yarmouth in the evening, to sleep on the beach or at Breydon Water. I didn't want to go back to Yarmouth. I'd got all I wanted, here, arm in arm with Trish.

We got over a style into a field with some cows in it. I held both her hands and jumped her down from the stile. We looked at the cows and they looked at us. They were all black-and-white except for one who was brown, and big with a thick neck. I looked at it again.

'Hey! That one's a *bull!*' I went.

'Full marks, Jeff,' Trish giggled. 'He's a bull. That's Pedro.' She didn't seem worried, so I tried to keep walking slowly across the field.

'But he's not *doing* nothing!' I said.

'What do you want him to do?' she laughed.

'Well, you know – do his job!'

'He has to wait till a heifer's ready for him,' she said, off-hand. 'He's just happy with their company now. A dozen girl-friends.'

'He doesn't mind us being here?' I asked her.

'Why should he? We don't count.'

But I was glad when we got over the stile on the far side of the field. From the other side of the fence I watched the bull, calmly munching grass.

'How do horses do it?' I asked her.

'Do what?' she said.

'Fuck,' I said. Well, she made me say it.

She shrugged and said she was in Holland once at a fuckfarm, watching the fuckhorses. I said that was rude but she said no, that just was the way the Dutch talked about it. She said the stallions didn't really have much fun. The mares had to have their shoes taken off because they might kick the stallions in the teeth. I said that figured.

But she was shy about walking up the Manor drive. She thought it might disturb the old lady.

'It's all right,' I insisted. 'She's let me have the pad. She didn't ask for the keys back.'

Well, I had found them in the pocket of that uniform jacket. Maybe she had just forgotten to ask for them.

'Anyway,' I said, 'she's deaf. She's probably

watching the telly. She won't hear us. And she *said* I could use the bed and it didn't matter if I wasn't married.'

'She said all that?' Trish queried.

'Yes. She seemed to be against people getting married.'

So we scrunched up the gravel drive, but really it was so weedy that it didn't make much noise. There was an earthy smell of shrubberies and a sweet, heavy smell of flowers hanging in the air. Trish took deep breaths, and said, 'Roses and honeysuckle.'

We could see no lights in the Manor house, but of course there were lots of rooms on the other side.

'The stables are this way,' I told Trish.

'Has she got horses?' she had to ask.

'I shouldn't think so.'

'If I had stables like these I'd keep them full of horses. Those big doors must be the coach house. I'd keep a coach.'

'Just wait and see what's inside.'

I opened the big doors. They were noisy, and Trish looked round anxiously. She was usually the confident one, but not now.

'Even if she hears us, I'll just say I've come to lock up and give the keys back,' I told her. 'Look, isn't she beautiful?'

'Oh, the car. Old, isn't it?'

'She's a 1931 4½ litre Bentley with an Amherst-Villiers supercharger. Don't you like her?'

'Oh yes. Yes, Jeff. I'll – I'll love her for your sake, Jeff.' And she gave my arm a loving squeeze, and that was all right really. I opened the door and helped her in, into the dark that smelled of old leather and dust. We sat in the back seat and we kissed, but she wouldn't let me go any further.

'Not now, Jeff. Not here. I'll tell you something. I'm

102

jealous of your beautiful car, just like you're jealous of Henry.'

'I'm not—'

'Oh yes you are, and you know it. Anyway, I want to see your pad.'

It was dark on the wooden stairs and there didn't seem to be any light switches, but that was all right too. We clung together as we felt our way up. The room at the top had two big skylight windows, one each side of the sloping roof. Through one you could see the bright evening sky over the marshes. Through the other the moon was coming up over trees. Under the roof, the room held the warmth of the summer day.

'It's lovely here, Jeff,' Trish said. 'What are you looking for?'

'A light switch.'

'It's nicer like this. A bit stuffy though. Can you open a window?'

I got one open and the smell of flowers came in. Trish breathed in again.

'Jasmine, too! And oh! Listen!'

I could only hear a bird cheeping away.

'Jeff, it's a *nightingale!*'

Somehow it was the nightingale that did it. She came up behind me at the window, put her arms round my chest and began to undo the buttons on that uniform jacket.

'It's a beautiful jacket, too, Jeff, but I think I like you better without it.' She gave a little gasp as she found I was wearing nothing underneath it. She threw it on the old sofa, and I turned round towards her and she let me take off her top and bra. And our upper bodies made contact like that, our mouths too. This was not the ice-cold statue I had met in the sea. And then it was easy enough for me to peel down

103

her jeans and pants, and she was all visible in the mix of moonlight and twilight in the warm room. But I was stuck in those breeches and thick boots.

'Horrible bovver boots!' she giggled. She made me sit down on the sofa, and there was a bit of a struggle to pull off the boots, my socks, and the policeman's breeches afterwards. And then nothing hid any part of either of us.

I reached out for her but she held out her hand to stop me. She picked up her jeans, felt in the pocket, took out the little cardboard packet with the sealed one inside, and opened them up.

'I hate putting those things on,' I said.

'I hate them too. But I'll do it for you. Stand!'

No problem. I wanted her so much. Expertly, as if she was doing one of her horsey things, she rolled the rubber sheath down over my erection.

'I hope I got a big enough one,' she giggled. 'Only just! A shame, isn't it? I love you, Jeff, but if there's one thing that stops a girl riding it's having a baby inside her. And I might have a nasty virus, mightn't I?' Nice of her to put it that way round! Then she threw herself into my arms.

But we both knew that we had all the night before us and there was no need to hurry. On that sofa we explored every inch of each other's bodies, those new found planets, and liked what we saw, what we felt, and what we tasted.

'Why does your skin taste salty?' I asked her.

'Yours does too. We were in the sea last night, remember?'

'It seems a long time ago.'

And then the playing had gone on long enough, and she suddenly said, 'Bed!' And, hand in hand, we went into that little bedroom and fell onto that bed. And who was above or below, inside or outside of each other, or whose limbs were whose, we could no longer tell. I remember she pulled a rough blanket over us, and we slept.

It was one of those dreams when you know you're dreaming. There was the beautiful, gleaming Bentley, parked on the Golden Mile, and I was going to give people rides in it. I was trying to get it started by cutting and crossing the electrical leads. Some girl, I think it must have been Zandra, not Trish, kept telling me to be quick because a copper was coming. Why did she say it in such a funny way? *Qu-ick! Qu-ick!*

'*KEEWICK! KEEWICK! KEEWICK!*'

I woke with a start and sat up – which was difficult because Trish was half on top of me in the narrow bed.

'*KEEWICK! KEEWICK! KEEWICK!*'

I knew I was awake now, but I could still hear that voice, loud and shrill. My heart was thudding.

'Trish, what is it?'

'Only an old owl, Jeff. Tawny owl. Go back to sleep.'

But I had to see what was making the noise. After all, I was going to live here, wasn't I? I slid out of bed and went to the sloping window, opening over the garden. There on the roof ridge, black against the starry sky, was a mop of feathers. It spread wide wings and flew off in the moonlight.

And now I heard another sound. Surely I'd heard it before.

Snip, snip, snip, snip-snip, snip.

I looked down into the moonlit rose-garden. I couldn't believe my eyes.

'Trish!' I called, soft but urgent. 'Come and look at this!'

Groaning sleepily, she came out of the little bedroom and joined me. I had to lift her up like a child, with my arms round her middle, to see out of the skylight.

'Look, down among the rose trees,' I told her quietly.

I felt Trish gasp, and I felt her heart begin to race.

'I don't believe in ghosts,' she said, not very firmly. I put her down, but kept holding her.

'You don't have to,' I told her. 'Unless that was a ghost I talked with this morning.'

'Yesterday, you mean. It must be long past midnight. What's she *doing* out there?'

'She's gardening, isn't she?'

'Perhaps she walks in her sleep. Oh, the poor old thing! Jeff, do you really think you can manage with her?'

'If I can manage with that owl I can manage with the old lady. So long as you're somewhere around, Trish.'

We went back to the narrow bed, and our playing began all over again, more serious this time, as if we really needed each other. Then we settled down to sleep again.

I felt her leave the bed in the morning, and to tell the truth I was glad to stretch out in it by myself for a bit. My legs were remembering that riding lesson. I heard her splashing at the little sink, and I thought dreamily that being married must be like this, somebody getting breakfast for you. I dozed off again. I'm not much good at getting up in the morning.

When I woke up again there were no noises. I called out to her sleepily but there was no reply. She'd gone! In a sort of panic I jumped out of bed – and felt naked, all by myself there in the flat. I went to the sink and splashed some water over myself, and then found there was nothing to dry myself on but the curtains. Then I saw the letters on the little table.

106

Two separate pages I was afraid to read them. Letters are usually bad news, aren't they?

They both had printed headings:

*RUSHBY MANOR FARM PEDIGREE HOLSTEIN
FRIESIAN HERD*

Trish must have brought them with her specially. That girl thought of everything! I wasn't sure I liked the look of the top one, though, it seemed sort of *official.*

To Whomsoever This May Concern (Where had she got *that* from?)

This is to certify that JEFFREY DOOLEY has shown no falling-off from his high standards of performance, and has given me complete satis-faction.

*(Signed) Patricia Niarchos-Jones
Farm Secretary.*

What was I supposed to make of that? Was it the final brush-off? I had asked for a reference, but I wanted more than that.

I looked at the other one. It was a bit of a scribble but a lot more friendly.

Sorry no brekky. I've got to go and feed the horses, come and share their hossmix! I love you, X Trish.

So that was all right, she'd even forgiven me for starving her again.

THE CONFIDENTIAL DIARY OF P. N-J

Friday May 29th

I'm trying to feel guilty but I can't. I had the lot, or nearly. Fabulous sunset (Fabulous? Yes, clouds like galloping centaurs). Scent of roses, honeysuckle and jasmine. A moon and even a nightingale. And a proper bed and all. All that was missing was the cornflakes – well, and the ring of course.

But I sort of wish it hadn't happened yet – not because it went wrong but because it went right. Chantal says sex isn't a Big Deal – but it *is*, and there's no going back from it. I know that now.

I'm hooked on this boy. But what am I hooked onto? Am I in love with a Hardened Criminal? Oh, I've got all sorts of wild scenarios for us, like he gets the Bentley bequeathed to him by the old lady, and he sets up as a restorer of vintage vehicles – but is this just what love does to your mind?

The question is, when it comes to the crunch again, which side will he be on? What if I had to choose between Jeff and Henry? That would be the crunch, wouldn't it?

7

Muckspreader

(Jeff's Story)

No, I didn't go to the stable for a hossmix breakfast.
I knew I'd got things to do. I'd got one reference
towards landing the job. Two more to go. I rode
back to Yarmouth and parked the bike. I'd left the
chauffeur's gear behind at the Manor, didn't want
people to think I'd done a copper.

Gary was loafing around the hostel.

'Look what's crawled in!' he said. 'Did you get the
job?' – but he said it like it was the last thing he
would believe.

'Of course,' I told him, smug as anything.

'Come off it!' he said. 'You spent the night with a
chick, didn't you?'

'That too,' I shrugged. 'Is Sam about?'

'In the office. You going to say you're sorry for
being a bad boy?'

'Going to ask him for a reference,' I said, really
cool. My mate Gary sort of exploded with laughter,
and wished me all the luck I deserved.

Sam's a fuddyduddy, of course, glasses and gingery
moustache, but I suppose he's all right really.

'You've got a straight-up offer of a job?' He eyed
me.

'Sure. With residential accommodation. Can you

give me a reference, Sam? You know, say I'm trust-worthy, honest, reliable and all that?'

'You must be joking, Jeff. It could cost me *my* job. But we'll see what we can do. I can't say I'd be sorry to lose you. I'm only too glad to get rid of any of you lot into the working world.' And he thumped me on the shoulder, hard.

'You lay a finger on me and I'll write to my MP,' I said.

'That'll be the day, Jeff Dooley, when you write a letter,' he laughed. 'Get out before I lay my boot on your arse!' Then he called me back.

'There's been a Mr Stanley White asking you to ring him. Seems *he's* got a job for you too. Runs a transport firm. How come you're so much in demand? I wish I was. I could do with a change from nannying layabouts like you.'

Hmmm! I kept my mouth shut about Stan White. Did I want to be in touch with him again? Hang on – he might give me my third reference, though! I counted through the coins in my pocket and reckoned I could stand myself some sort of breakfast and a phone call. I wasn't going to use the hostel phone with Sam and everyone listening.

It's quite a walk to Rosie Lee's at the dockside but the grub's cheap and I like the company. There was even live music coming out, at eleven o'clock in the morning! You can tell when it's live, can't you? Sounds sort of weedy.

I walked in. The so-called music was Patent Muck-spreader, the folk group. I don't go much on that sort of stuff, especially in the early morning. I don't know why they were playing. Perhaps they'd gone on all night and couldn't stop.

'Turn the amp down, Phil!' I said. 'I want to make a phone call.'

Whiskery Paul stopped squeaking on his fiddle and said, 'This is an important rehearsal for the gig in aid of Hunt Sab, but your contributions will be gratefully received. We've got some new traditionals to practise. You'll notice we are unamplified.'

They went on playing and I reckoned that at least no one could overhear my phone call. I ordered tea and double chips, put a few coins in and pressed the buttons. I was lucky to get Stan White straight away.

''allo, Jeff boy! Nice to see you, it was, at the races. Like I told you, we got to keep in touch. Have we got crossed lines or are you at a party? I keep hearing music.'

I told him all my parties go on for twenty-four hours, and let him talk.

'How about next Saturday, not the coming Saturday, one after that? I could do with a bright young lad with your qualifications for that little job again. Same time same place, eh? I expect you remember, Rushby it's called. See you there, eh? Don't worry, I'll make it worth your while.'

Without thinking much I said, 'OK Stan, I'll help you if you help me. I need a reference for a job. Send it round to the hostel, could you? And I'll see you at those stables, right? I – er – took a good look at them last time.'

I heard Stan laughing and saying, 'A reference, you say? You're never going *straight* are you, boy? OK, it's a deal – ' and the pips went.

I'd been starving hungry when I walked in, but now there was a cold feeling in my belly and I sat and looked at the greasy pile of chips. *I expect you remember, Rushby it's called.* *My* Rushby! I knew they didn't want the likes of Stan there. And something dreadful might happen to my Trish and her Henry.

111

The Muckspreaders took a break for barleymix or whatever muck they drank. Fifi, the nice girl who plays the penny whistle, sat down at my table. She'd been my girlfriend once, and – for once – we had parted friends, when she discovered she was a bit older than me.

'Not eating your nice chips, Jeff?'

I pushed the plate across to her. 'Help yourself, Feef.' She did.

'What's eating you?' she asked.

'Nothing you can help with,' I grunted.

'Never underestimate the power of a woman,' she said.

Then it hit me. Perhaps she could help. I wasn't sure exactly how.

'What was that you're rehearsing for?' I asked.

'Hunt Sabotage. I do a bit of it in the winter. And we have to do things to keep together in the summer. Gigs and Animal Lib demos.'

I reached the chips back. I needed fuel for the next bit.

'You know those people who export live horses for meat?' I began. I didn't know whether Stan did this, but I suspected it.

'It's illegal now,' she said. 'But some of the things they do aren't much better. What about them?'

'Listen, Fiona. They'll be loading a truckful of horses at Rushby early next Saturday. Would your people like to do some liberating?'

Her eyes lit up. 'Just what we need! We'd love to. Tell me the details.'

I told her the details, and she borrowed a pen and wrote them down on the palm of her hand. And then Whiskery Phil struck up again, and I walked out onto the dockside.

What have I started? I asked myself as I walked

112

back past the moored ships. Letting loose the Animal Libbers on Trish's stable! Mightn't they be more dangerous than Stan White's inefficient gang? Why didn't I just go to the police about it?

Plenty of reasons why not. One, they wouldn't believe me. Two, villains like Stan can be hard on grasses. And all my other offences to be taken into consideration, as they say in the courts.

I thought it might take a day or two to get those references and I'd better take the bike back to its stable for a while. I chugged along the streets of semis, waved towards the neighbours as usual, rode into the drive and opened the door of the shed. Then I had the shock of my life. A woman came out of the kitchen door and stared at me. I'd got so used to that house being empty that I hadn't bothered to look for any signs of occupation. But at least she'd caught me putting it back, not taking it away.

She was a sloppy sort of blonde, in a shell suit and bedroom slippers, with a cigarette in the corner of her mouth.

'What have you got there?' she asked. She seemed more interested in me than in the bike. I collected my wits and played it cool.

'Your gent's bike,' I said. 'I've done a thorough overhaul, oil change, checked the systems, brakes, the lot.' And this was true.

'He don't tell me nothing,' she said. 'Anything to pay?'

'Dyke's Bikes will send you their account, madam,' I said, really brassing it out now. 'That'll include VAT of course. Unless you happen to have twenty five quid cash?'

'Is that all?' she said, looking insulted. 'Hang on, I'll get my purse.' And she went indoors. Was she fetching her man? Or phoning the police? It needed

113

steady nerves, waiting there, but it was worth it. She came out with a twenty and a five, handed them to me, gave me a smile that tried to be sexy, and went in. Didn't ask for a receipt or anything. It's criminal, the way some women hand out money! And I kicked myself for not asking double. After all, I had maintained that bike for months. But maybe I had pitched it about right. I had cash in my pocket.

But I'd got no transport now. Rushby suddenly seemed a long way away. I had to get myself settled in at the manor, and at the wheel of that Bentley. I walked back to the hostel and there was nobody about, but there were two letters in my pigeonhole. One was in a Social Services envelope, the other in a brown envelope with lubricating oil on it, which I opened. Stan White had kept his part of the deal, so things were moving! There was nothing to keep me in Yarmouth now. I put both letters in my pocket to read later, found some plastic carrier bags in the kitchen and went upstairs and stuffed my things into them. There wasn't much that was heavy, except for the old set of tools that Grandpa had given me. And I walked out of that hostel, with nobody to say goodbye to. I felt bad about missing Gary – but perhaps it was just as well that even he couldn't trace me. I'd make it up to him some time, drive out to see him in the Bentley, then he'd have to believe in the job.

I started walking towards the bus station. Me, taking a bus! I felt a wally, carrying those plastic bags through the town. People would think I'd been to Tesco's! And those tools got heavier and heavier.

At the bus station I asked about buses to Rushby and the man said, 'Twice a week.' I told him to stop taking the mickey. He didn't smile or anything, just told me there were two a day to Haddiscoe and I could walk from there. One had just gone. He offered

114

me a timetable but I told him what he could do with it and walked out. I began to wonder how far poor Trish had to walk that evening, and it made me feel rotten, and I longed to see her.

There was a taxi rank. I walked up to it.

'Where to?' the surly driver asked.

'Rushby Manor,' I snapped.

'Certainly, squire!' he mocked me, looking at my plastic bags.

'How much?' I asked.

'To Rushby Manor? Where in hell's that?'

'It's your job to know, isn't it? I'll pay you half fare if I have to navigate. Other side of Haddiscoe.'

'There and back?'

'No, I live there.'

He looked at me more closely.

'Twenty pound, guvnor.'

'So I'll give you ten, and tell you the way.'

'Look, I'm not one of your Third World cabbies. Don't you haggle with me!'

I took a closer look at his taxi. Patches of rust round the wheel arches. And the tyres! I found a measure in my toolcase and tested the thin tread.

'Just about safe, but not legal,' I told him.

'Get in, mate,' he said. 'You might have said you were in the trade. Ten pounds.'

He helped me put my bags in the boot but I took my toolkit on the back seat with me. Funny, being a passenger! He was a rotten driver and the car was in poor nick, but he was being careful. He would get me there.

I pulled out four letters from my pocket. I started with the shortest one, Trish's:

Sorry no brekky. I've got to go and feed the horses, come and share their hossmix. I love you, X Trish.

I gave it a kiss. I would see her again soon! I looked at her reference. *No falling off ... performance ...*

115

has given me satisfaction . . . For the first time I saw the cheeky meanings, and the taxi driver turned round to see what I was laughing at.

I opened the official looking envelope, pulled out the letter and read it – or tried to.

Social Service officers are not empowered to issue open character assessments of persons for whom they have statutory responsibility. Notwithstanding, officers may present themselves as personal referees in the context of applications for employment, subject to conditions of strict confidentiality.

Oh yes? They could say all that again! Was it a reference or wasn't it? Hell, it was a bit of official bumf and it might frighten the old lady more than it frightened me.

What had Stan White come up with? It was written on an invoice form, headed SPACEWIDE TRANS-PORT SERVICE, Prop. S. White. That was all right. Underneath he'd scrawled something in block capitals, like this:

JEFFREY DOOLEY

DRIVES ME CRAZY AT TIMES BUT
WELL, HE IS YOUNG AND HE IS A
WILLING LAD. GIVE HIM A FAIR
CUT AND HE WONT NEVER
GRASS ON YOU. BUT DONT BELIEVE
TOO MUCH IN WHAT HE TELL YOU.

STAN WHITE.

The old bastard! What was the use of that to me? It was one villain's tip-off to another, wasn't it? I nearly hurled it out of the window, then I thought it was my last hope. Could I re-write it somehow? I

116

stared at the words until I gave up, and folded it to shove it back in the oily envelope.

It was folded in a funny way. I could only see the first words in each line:

JEFF

DRIVES
WELL,
WILL
CUT
GRASS
TOO

STAN

That might do! Nobody else had said I could drive and do useful things. I flattened out the paper again. But what to do with all the other words? Even if I whited them out with some of that Tippex stuff it wouldn't look right.

And then I had another of my brilliant ideas. I knew I had a passport photograph of myself in my wallet – four of us had had a go in and out of a Photo-Me machine for a lark. I pulled it out and put it over the words I didn't want. Better than I hoped!

JEFFREY DOOLEY

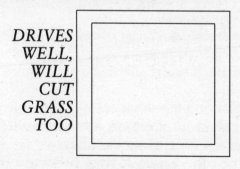

DRIVES
WELL,
WILL
CUT
GRASS
TOO

STAN WHITE

117

I found some rubber solution in my toolkit, stuck the picture on – and there you go, Jeff Dooley! I spent the rest of the journey daydreaming of me chauffeuring the old lady, plus Trish of course, to garden parties at Sandringham.

The taxi drove along those lanes I'd got lost in and I did my best to remember the turnings without having to ask the rabbits. Then we were going up the drive and stopping by the Manor. The driver looked at me with respect.

'This where you live, squire?'

'Of course.' I dumped my toolcase and plastic bags on the weedy gravel and handed him a tenner. I didn't want his old banger littering up the drive for too long. He made a grimace at the note.

'Give my love to Count Dracula,' he said, and drove off.

I carried my things to the garage – I'd still got the key – and went to the house with my references. I rang the doorbell. Nothing happened. I rang again. Nothing happened for a long time, again.

I walked round to the back door. There she was, the old lady, sitting at the kitchen table putting flowers in a jug. I rapped at the back door. Nothing happened. I rapped at the kitchen window, which was partly open, and she looked round.

'Kindly go to the back door!' she called out haughtily. After a bit she opened it to me.

'The electricity meter's under the back stairs there,' she said.

I stood there, not knowing what to say. She didn't seem to recognize me at all. Perhaps she was having a bad day. My old nan used to be like that.

'I've come for the job,' I said loudly, holding out the references. She peered at the envelopes.

118

'My spectacles are in the kitchen. Please wait there.' And she took the papers indoors. I waited in the sun and listened to the birds. They seemed to be mocking me. Had everything started to go wrong?

She was back at the door squinting at the letters through thick specs.

'So you're Mr Jeffrey Dooley? Have I seen you before somewhere?'

I took a deep breath and spoke as loud and as clear as I knew how.

'Yes madam.' (Had I ever called anyone madam before? The word sounded funny in my mouth.) 'You promised me the chauffeur job if I could produce three references.'

'Oh? Oh, *did* I? Of course, references. My son always insists on references. He's a lawyer, you know. In New Zealand.'

She poked her old nose into the papers while I blessed all those thousands of miles that kept that lawyer son from seeing my references.

'They certainly seem all right. You've worked for the Social Security? They're the people who pay me my pension, aren't they? Perhaps you could advise me about these things. And you've worked on a farm so you must be used to the country. And this one with the snapshot says you do gardening. Well now, there's plenty of grass to cut. Do you wish to live in? Perhaps you had better see the Bentley and the accommodation.'

'I saw them last time, madam. Very satisfactory.' I was acting the part, I hoped.

'Last time? Ah, yes it's coming back to me. You're the one with the motorbike, the Harley-Davidson chain-drive model. Is it going well?'

'I have disposed of it, madam. I hope to spend my time on the Bentley.'

'My dear man, if you can get *her* on the road you'll be in my good books for ever. Now I come to think of it we did agree on terms. Start whenever it suits you, Dooley.'

So that's how it went. I saw her put the letters in a jam jar on the kitchen shelf and I breathed a sigh of relief and moved into the chauffeur's pad officially. I tried to stop myself sitting and dreaming about the night I'd spent there with Trish.

I just had to see her again. As I walked across the fields to the stables I wondered what to tell her about Stan and the Libbers. It had to be everything, I decided. No more secrets between us.

Joanna who owns the stables was in the yard with two or three little kids. She said hello to me in a friendly way.

'You're Jeff, aren't you, Trish's friend? It was ever so kind of you to drive her to Burlingham the other day. And I hear you got on all right on Nelson.'

'Is Trish here?' I asked.

'No, she's gone back to school.'

'*School?*' I was so amazed, I said it out loud. Trish at school!

'Yes, you know, that sixth form she goes to in Norwich. Keeps her really busy in term time, with all the homework and studying. Of course she can't help with the stables like she does in the holidays but she comes round evenings and weekends. Can I give her a message?'

Tell her I love her. No, I hadn't the nerve to say that.

'If you see her, could you tell her I got the job?'

'Oh, that sounds good! Er – is this the job at the manor?' Her ears were flapping. Trish must have been talking to her about it, but I didn't mind. I said yes.

120

'Well, good luck! I hope you don't find it too lonely there. You've got a motorbike, haven't you?'

'No, it's – er, it's gone back to my friend. I was just looking after it.'

Joanna said, 'Sort of meat for manners, eh?'

'Pardon?'

'Meat for manners. That's what we say about horses. When somebody lets out a horse on loan and the other person feeds it and schools it. Like Trish does with Henry. She's done ever such a good job with him. Poor girl, she really deserves a horse of her own.'

So Henry wasn't Trish's, any more than that bike had been mine! Come to think of it, she'd never said he was. That made two of us! And it gave me something to say to the next copper who stopped me: *No, it's not my bike, I've got it meat for manners.*

Joanna pressed on: 'But you've got this old car to drive? Everyone's heard of it but nobody's seen it.'

'I haven't got her on the road yet.'

'So you're on foot. You'd better borrow a horse!' she laughed.

'I need a bit of practice.'

'Good! And Nelson needs the exercise. Whenever you can fix it with Trish, eh?' And she wheeled her muck-barrow away and I turned back towards the manor.

I did some thinking on the way back. I hadn't seen Trish but I'd learned two things about her. She wasn't all that rich, and she still went to school. *You're rotten, Jeff Dooley,* I told myself. *If you really loved that girl you'd find out more about her. You don't even ask!*

And I might have to gnaw my own fingernails for a bit longer without telling anybody about the rustlers. Fingernails wouldn't keep me alive, though. I'd have to do something about food, but I'd got no sense out of the old lady this morning. I must try again. I went to the back door and knocked, very loud. It was opened almost at once by a strong slim woman with a broom. She was wearing an apron and she had blonde hair and piercing blue eyes.

'No need to knock the bloody door down!' she said, quite friendly. 'You must be Jeffrey. I'm Brigitte, call me Budgie. I done out your flat this morning. Right pootrid, it was. You'd be surprised some of the things I swep' up off that floor. Is there suffen else I can do for you?'

I gave her a macho grin but my heart wasn't in it. There was only one woman for me now. I went straight to the point.

'I like to eat sometimes. What's the arrangement, Budgie?'

'Aha! Well, Toosdays Joanna come round with Meals on Wheels, but you look a bit young to be untitled to that. I come in Mondays, Wednesdays and Fridays to see she's still alive and kicken. She's mostly kicken. There's the travellin' grocery come Mondays and Fridays and you can stock yourself up then. I leave her suffen hot, days I'm here.'

'So you'll do suffen for me?' She'd got me talking that way now.

'Not bloody likely, boy!' she grinned. 'But I tell you what. Me and my mum and dad run the Social Club round the corner. Come round there evenings, and we'll do you steak and chips, scampi, fill you up proper any time. You'll get moosic. And my dad run a breakin' yard too, so if you want any spares you know where to go.'

'Thanks. How do I get money out of the old girl?'

'Beat her over the head with a broom till she pay up,' she grinned.

'Doesn't she go out shopping?' I asked.

'Her go shoppen? She never go anywhere!'

'What does she need a chauffeur for, then?' I asked.

'Doon't ask me, boy. Thass your problem! But this woon't do. I've got my little girl to collect from school, and the van not come yet.' She whipped off her apron and revealed skin-tight pink jeans, and then there was a scrunching on the gravel and a tatty van drove up. Budgie bought some things. I counted out my cash and bought packets of crisps and a pork pie.

I ate them in the pad, drank some water and went down and had a good look over the old car, with the big doors letting in plenty of daylight. She was up on blocks, standing over an inspection pit. The tyres were soft but they might be all right. I opened up the bonnet. Battery? Where was it? There didn't seem to be one in any of the places where you'd expect to find a battery, but there must be one somewhere. Was there a manual? I looked in the glove compartment, and yes, there was something as thick as a Bible. I sat down on the front seat with it. I'm not one for reading much but I can find my way through a manual. The battery was somewhere behind the back axle! I got down the pit and found it. It had to be flat, but I was surprised to find it had been kept topped up, so it might be rechargeable.

Tools? I had my own but I had the feeling that nothing would fit. I took a look round the old coach house. A great solid workbench, drenched in old oil but tidy. Massive old vices attached to it. And racks and racks of old mechanic's tools, things that nobody uses now like oilcans with long nozzles, and grease-guns, and a big brass foot-pump. They were all clean and hanging on their proper pegs like in a museum. I couldn't make out why people hadn't broken in and nicked them all.

123

There was even an old suit of overalls hanging on a nail. It was very oily, but better than nothing, so I put it on over my T-shirt and jeans. I had another look at the outside of the engine. It looked like the sort of shiny machine they have on the counter in caffs to make coffee with, no dirt or grease, just dust and cobwebs. But what was it like inside? That thing must be the dipstick. It would tell me. I pulled it up, and the end showed just the right amount of lovely clear, clean oil. Somebody besides me loved this engine. Surely not the old lady? Water? The radiator was like a huge honeycomb. I unscrewed the shiny cap with a B on it, and saw it had been drained. And when I found the petrol tank, that was clean and empty too. It had lettering on it saying 'Capacity 25 gallons.' Fill her up for fifty quid! Of course they say petrol used to be 10p a gallon, but I can't really believe that.

The question was, could I get this car on the road by Saturday week? I felt I was going to need transport then. So where did I start? There was a trickle-charger circuit on the wall over the bench. I could get the battery jizzed up, couldn't I? I heaved the big heavy battery out and connected it up. That would take a bit of time. Meanwhile I could get oiling and greasing. I looked at the greasiest page of the manual, where it showed you all the places that you had to 'oil weekly' and 'grease monthly'. Everywhere there were little nipples, and you had to fit the end of the grease gun over them and push until the grease came out of the joint. I enjoyed doing that.

Everything took time, but I hardly noticed how time passed, except that the sunbeams from the door moved over the floor. And then, while I was down the pit there was a moving shadow in the patch of sunlight. A voice called.

124

'Jeff?'

I dropped the grease gun, straightened up and knocked my head on the differential casing, and clambered out of the pit.

In the doorway stood a schoolgirl in a neat navy uniform and snow-white blouse. The sun lit up her loose blonde hair. But I was used to Trish's changes of shape, and I ran towards her. Then stopped.

'Aren't you pleased to see me?' she asked.

I looked down at my oily, dusty overalls and greasy hands.

'I'm in a right old mess!'

She craned her neck forward and extended her lips for me to kiss. I did the same, and only our lips met, plus a few strands of hair. It was quite exciting enough.

'Go back to your Joy, Jeff,' she laughed. 'I suppose I ought to ask how she is.'

'Who?'

'Joy. That's her name isn't it? She's got it on the front.'

'Oh, you mean the car? She's better than I thought. I've got the battery on trickle-charge and I'm doing the lube and grease routine and I reckon I can get the tyres up to pressure though I'll have to find a gauge and check the spess. But these vehicles never had no built-in obsolescence.'

'Oh?' she said. 'Good. I'd better leave you to it. I just had to see you.' And she turned away.

'Don't go!' I pleaded. 'I've got a lot to tell you. Sit in the back with me, Trish!' I struggled out of my overalls.

But she said she'd been indoors all day and would rather talk outside. So we did, as we walked towards Manor Farm. They had been cutting hay in one of the fields and making those square bales. She jumped over each one as we came to it.

'I don't know what you need a pony for if you can jump like that,' I told her. 'Let's sit down so you can listen.'

'Promise to behave?'

'All right, I'm not fooling.' We sat on a hay bale – and then I found it hard to start.

'Listen, Trish. That first morning when we met. You never asked me what I was doing there at the stables.'

'Didn't I? I suppose I thought you'd dropped from heaven. You said something about Steve – Stu? – Stan?'

'That's right, Stan White. I – I've done a few little jobs for him, changing number plates and that. I never asked questions. I didn't know what he wanted me to do that morning, honest. But he's asked me again, and Trish, he's a real villain.'

She shot me a straight look. 'So what's the problem, Jeff? Have nothing more to do with him! You've got a straight job now.'

'You don't understand, Trish. He could go ahead without me, easy enough. Ever heard of horse rustling?'

'Oh no!' She was really shocked. 'Not – not at our stables?'

So I told her all I knew, which wasn't much for certain. She jumped up.

'I'll ring the police right away!'

'No, Trish, no! Do me a favour, not the cops!'

'Whyever not?'

'Do you want to get me nicked? It would all have to come out, the things I did before. And anyway we've nothing hard to tell them, nothing that they'll believe. What's more, if Stan hears of it, Jeff gets done over for grassing – do you want that?'

She sat down again, but all tense.

'So what do we do?'

And I told her about the Hunt Sabbers. I didn't know how she would take it. She laughed.

'That lot? Crazy lot of hippies! Mind you, I sometimes think they're right, what they *say* about hunting.'

That was a surprise, and a relief.

'I thought all you horsey people loved slaughtering the old foxes.'

'It's hares round here, not foxes, and hares don't eat chickens, do they? I've been out for a gallop with the hounds twice. The first time we killed nothing, but the sabbers came and I felt like killing them for the way they frightened the horses. The second time – yuk – I heard a hare screaming for mercy as four dogs pulled it to pieces. I felt I could join the Sabbers.'

'Perhaps they'll frighten Stan White's gang,' I said. 'Tell me I haven't really screwed things up.'

She was standing up, stretching her arms in the sun and laughing again in a fierce sort of way. 'Looks like we're going to have some fun, Saturday week! I'll put it in my diary.' Then she was walking away and leaping over more hay bales, so I asked her where she was going.

'Home. I mean back to Manor Farm.'

I caught up with her.

'Trish,' I said. 'I want to be really straight with everybody. I want to meet your people.'

'People?' she repeated, strangely.

'Your Mum and Dad, Trish.'

She looked away. 'It would be difficult, Jeff.'

'Oh, I've thought about it a lot. They won't think much of me, I know. But I've got to meet them some time. Why not now? Will they be there? Does your dad work that farm, or just own it?'

'I told you, Jeff. My dad's a Greek sailor, second engineer or something. You'd get on with him all right. I see him once or twice a year, with luck. He's taken me on trips, like that one to Holland. It's always fun. My mum died.'

Oh God! How clumsy I'd been again! I stammered that I was sorry.

'You don't have to say things like that, it happened a long time ago. I'm lucky. I'm sort of fostered by the Joneses. They were going to adopt me but then their own kids started coming along. I like it that way, and now I can help with the farm business.'

'You signed that letter "Farm Secretary"! I thought it was a joke.'

'It's no joke. I do a lot of their forms and accounts now. I'm going to be a rich accountant and spend all my money on horses.'

I was silent for a bit, then I blurted it all out.

'I told you I lived in a hotel. It wasn't a hotel, I was in care in a Council hostel. My dad's in jail and I don't know where my mum is. I've got a police record, and that Saturday morning I had decided to nick your horses. I'm not the sort of person you thought I was.'

She stopped and faced me in the middle of that hayfield.

'The trouble is, Jeff, you *are* the sort of person I thought you were all along – though I think you're nicer than you think you are. I'm glad you told me straight out, but it makes no difference. You know what it does mean, don't you, Jeff? It means nobody cares much what happens to either of us, except ourselves. And there's nobody else we can go to and say "Look what you made me do!" '

'Right,' I said. 'It's not fair, Trish, is it?'
'It's not fair,' she grinned. 'But it can be fun!'

THE CONFIDENTIAL DIARY OF P. N-J

Friday May 29th

So that was my half-term break. Back to the sixth
form college again and people asking, 'Did you have
a nice holiday?' (Yes thanks I went to Pleasure Beach.)
Now I've got an economics essay to finish. 'A scarce
resource is one for which the demand at a zero price
would exceed the available supply. Give examples.' A
1931 Bentley? How am I going to settle down to this
sort of thing again? Yet I've got to. It's my only road
towards earning enough salary to keep a top grade
show horse, which I've always wanted to do. But I'm
not the same person that I always was.

(Later) The Crunch may come sooner than I
expected. He's Come Clean! Confessions of a Horse
Rustler Shock Horror!

No, it wasn't all that much of a shock, I think I'd
got his character sussed out days ago. I'd guessed he
was a joyrider – but why did he have to turn out a
horse rustler on top of that? Well, he says he's never
rustled a horse yet – but his gang are planning another
job, *and Henry's to be the victim.* Not to worry, he
says, he's got it all stitched up! Of course I ought to
call out the police, the army, the Bungay Gun Club!
But he says that will only land him in the nick and
I've got to trust him.

Have I got to choose between him and Henry?

8

The Manor

(Jeff's Story)

I woke up alone in that chauffeur's pad.

Oh, you want the going to bed bit again? I went to bed alone too. It wasn't what either of us really wanted and we had a bit of an argument about it. Our first quarrel.

I said, 'The old lady told me not to think about getting married, just get stuck in on the job.'

Trish said, 'Old people speak a different language to us. I'm sure she meant the chauffeur's job, and she didn't want women around.'

I said, 'Can she *do* that to us?'

Trish said, 'She can give you the sack, Jeff. Don't let's push our luck with her yet.' Then she said she had to write an essay – whatever *that* is.

So there I was, that evening, pretty knackered after a day dismantling the Bentley's engine and memorizing how to put it together again. I don't know about studying, but what I was doing was brainwork, too, wasn't it? So, well, really I needed that narrow bed to myself that night.

I took off my walkman and there was nothing but the night noises to listen to. Wind noises in the trees. Scuttling noises in the old roof. Birds? *Rats?* Moaning noises from far away, but that could be just a cow.

There was nothing around me but empty country. If I listened hard enough I could hear traffic noises from the A road, even the rattle of a train going across the marshes, but these sounds were so quiet and distant that it made me feel all the lonelier. Not a human being for miles!

But there was. The old lady, across the yard, alone in the big house.

How could she stand it? Of course, she would have her Things for company. I hadn't been further than the old-fashioned kitchen but I had a picture in my head of what the rest of the house would look like. I had watched a few classy soaps on the telly, and when I was a kid my grandpa once took me round that place with a miniature railway – Somerleyton Hall, isn't it? But how could the old lady live alone in a place like that, when there were villains out there just waiting to get their hands on her Things? Villains like . . .

Like me for instance!

I had this thought: *if anything goes missing, guess who'll get the rap? Dooley!*

I drifted off into sleep and dreams. There I was with Trish, inside the manor, entertaining our guests, who were all wearing jods and riding hats. They were gawping at our Things: crystal chandeliers hanging from the ceilings, pictures in solid gold frames on the walls, red velvet curtains with gold tassels, furniture with crooked gold arms and legs, magic carpets on the floor. Trish kept telling the guests to wipe their wellies on the doormat. We moved into the big dining hall where the long table was laid for dinner. But instead of gold and silver spoons and forks and plates there were car wheels and tyres, bits of engine and spanners scattered over the table. I was saying it was

131

all right, I'd soon get them put together if people would help . . .

I woke up in the morning alone, and the dream had made my mind up about one thing. I did need help over that engine.

'If you need supplies for the job, use the telephone in the hall,' the old lady told me. She was right on, when it came to talking about the car, was old Mrs Campbell. I'd at least discovered her name, a bit ordinary. I'd been expecting The Honourable Lady Something. Well, if I was to get on with the job, I was going to ring Grandpa. He'd be tickled to death to help, and he'd probably get on with Mrs C.

After I'd dressed and made myself a bit of breakfast I crossed the yard to the back door of the manor. It was a windy, grey, rainy morning. 'You needn't disturb me,' she'd said. I tried the door and it opened. 'Go along the passage from the kitchen,' she'd said.

Nothing very wonderful in the passage, worn-out wellies and smelly old gardening clothes hanging up. At the end of it, a door covered in tatty green cloth. Beyond it, there must be the grand rooms of the manor.

I pushed the door open, and it creaked on its hinges. The big hall, rather dark and gloomy. A staircase at one end, and doors leading off it, and, yes, the telephone, standing like a candlestick on a wooden box. I could phone, but I felt cheated. I hadn't seen any grand Things yet. They certainly didn't keep them in the hall.

No harm in peeping? I felt sort of *responsible* for this grand house, so I needed to know what I was responsible for, didn't I?

That big door opposite the stairs must lead outside, mustn't it? I'd try the grand double doors on the left. They must lead to something big. I shut my eyes as I

132

gave the door a push, because I wanted to see all the rich Things at once when I opened them. I could even see them with my eyes shut: the glittering chandeliers, the glowing pictures and carpets, the gleaming furniture . . .

I opened my eyes, and at first they didn't believe what they saw. I was looking across a long stretch of bare wooden floor to the far end of the room. Why did they have such an ugly big fireplace of raw, sooty bricks? Tall windows let in the grey morning light, but where were the velvet curtains? Why were there square patches on the papered walls, instead of gorgeous pictures? Why were there no magic carpets on the floor, only squares of unpolished wood?

I walked to the other end of the room, trying not to make too much noise on the bare boards. I looked closer at the fireplace. Those marks on the brickwork had been made by wrecking-bars. I've done demolition work – more for the fun than the money – so I knew. There must have been a marble fireplace here like the front of a Lloyds bank. Some one – some gang – had ripped it out, and they'd not been too fussy about making good afterwards.

Don't panic, Dooley! And why should I panic? It was nothing to do with me. But I had to know what the full score was. I went back to the hall and opened a door into another room, not quite so big. Just as empty. The walls were in a shocking state, all bare plaster and nail holes. What had there been here? What do they call it? Panelling. All gone. And another wrecked fireplace.

I went back to the hall and up the stairs. At least they'd left the stairs, though there were more bare patches on the walls instead of pictures.

On the landing I saw the body.

And – this was the sick bit – there was a book sort

133

of propped up on the body. And the words on the book said MURDER MOST FOUL.

Run for it, Dooley! Don't get mixed up in this any more!

But I walked quietly down the stairs to that telephone. I dialled the three numbers on the local exchange. I suppose I was lucky to get Trish straight away.

'Trish, I'm in the manor house. Can you come over straight away?'

'But Jeff, I've got to go to school!'

'School can wait. Do you want me to get done for robbery and murder?'

I heard her gasp, and then say, 'I'll come on my bike.'

As I walked back along the passage to the kitchen I started thinking about fingerprints, footprints. How many had I left, and where? The police knew my fingerprints. So it was no use running away. But I let myself out of the house and started walking down Long Road to meet Trish.

We met halfway down. She hadn't wasted any time, not even put a raincoat on, that rainy morning. Her hair was wild and unbrushed.

'Oh Jeff, what's it all about?'

'I can't explain. You'd better come and see. There's been a big job!'

She pedalled and I ran, and we were soon back at the Manor, out of breath. I led the way through the back door.

'This door wasn't locked, that's how I got in. She *said* I could use the phone.'

I let the way down the passage and into the hall, and quickly showed her the two wrecked rooms.

'Have you brought me here just to see empty rooms?' Trish demanded.

'They're not just empty,' I told her. 'They've been stripped, gutted. I know the signs. I didn't *do* it, Trish, you've got to believe me!'

She stared at me, then she burst out laughing! That silvery laugh of hers really cheered up the creepy old house.

'Oh Jeff, I know you're a superman and you may be a master criminal. But not even you could empty a house like this all by yourself. And sweep up the dust afterwards.'

She was right. Something had been worrying me about this robbery. Too tidy. Some villains are tidier than others, but this was weird.

I was a bit narked at being laughed at, though.

'Right, so I couldn't have done,' I said. 'But you can laugh. You don't know what it's like to be on the police books. They'll try and pin something on me.'

'You said murder. That's why I came.'

I took her by the arm. 'Come up the stairs. Have you ever seen a body?'

She did cling to me after I said that. We went up the broad stairs together. There was quite a lot of grey light coming in from a big landing window. As our heads reached the level of the landing, there it was, plain to see, flat out on the floorboards. The body of Mrs Campbell. There was the book, MURDER MOST FOUL.

The body turned over a page.

The hair on my neck sort of stood on end. For a moment, I couldn't move my legs, but Trish unhooked herself and went up the last few steps.

'Are you all right, Mrs Campbell?' Trish asked, speaking loud like you do to deaf people.

'Is there somebody there?' Mrs Campbell began. 'Yes, I'm perfectly all right, thank you very much.'

135

She put down her book and looked at us over her specs.

'Er – why are you lying there, Mrs Campbell?' Trish asked. It seemed a good question.

'You're not the District Nurse are you? Or the Health Visitor? Or the Ambulance people?'

'No, Mrs Campbell. This is, – er, Mr Dooley, your chauffeur, you know. And I'm Patricia. Can we do anything to help?'

'Patricia, eh? So you found your Patricia, Dooley? I'm so glad, she seems a thoroughly nice gal.' Well, she wasn't dead, thank God, and I thought *Funny, the things she remembers and the things she doesn't!* And she went on, lying flat on the floor with a bit too much of her old skinny legs showing, as if she was chatting with her lady friends over cups of tea. 'I am only lying here because I am unable to get up. I had a bit of a fall, but no bones broken, I believe. Nothing unusual and I'm used to it. I always carry a paperback book in my pinny pocket, to while away the time on the floor. This one is by Agatha Christie, I've probably read it dozens of times. Well, if you would be so kind as to assist me to my feet, we might move to more comfortable quarters in the kitchen.'

So Trish and I lifted her to her feet, one on each side of her, and it was like picking up a few dried sticks. We held her arms as we all went down the stairs, though she kept saying she was perfectly all right, and along the narrow passage to the kitchen she was managing with just a little support from Trish. We sat her in a wooden armchair, and Trish fussed around finding a kettle and a tin of tea, Mrs Campbell nattering on all the time about how nice it was to see a gal in a neat skirt and blouse. As I got cups and saucers down from the shelves, Trish

136

muttered, 'It may not be *tactful* to ask her about her things. Maybe she just had to sell them.'

Tactfulness? I'm not sure what that means. I thought I was entitled to ask, and I put it to her straight.

'Mrs Campbell, what happened to all your things?'

Trish made a face at me but Mrs Campbell was quite happy to tell us. 'My things? Well, they took them all, didn't they? Lock stock and barrel, clean sweep, stem to stern. Before it happened I had to go into hospital. I didn't want to go, I was perfectly all right at home, and of course I was worried about the house and things while I was away, but they insisted and took me in the ambulance to Norwich. And I believe no sooner was the ambulance away down the drive than the thieves drove up with one of those articulated trucks. Two, perhaps. They had all the time in the world to do the job. People saw them there and assumed I was dead or was selling up, so they didn't question anything. They broke the news to me in the hospital. At first I couldn't believe that *everything* was gone, books, jewellery, photograph albums, my wedding dress, everything, all my past life. But then – do you know? – I lay there in that hospital bed and I felt *free!* The worst had happened and I had nothing more to worry about. The people who eventually got my things would probably look after them much better than I could. I still had a roof over my head, and more room to myself in the kitchen than most poor families have for dozens of children. They didn't bother to strip the kitchen. And here we are, having a cosy cup of tea. Oh, Patricia, would you mind giving pussy a saucer of milk?'

'When did all this happen, Mrs Campbell?' I asked her.

She came over vague again. 'When? Don't ask me

137

when, dear man! You see, they took all my clocks, of course. And the wireless and the television. They even took the calendars – I had some rather beautiful ones. So time sort of ran out after that, I don't bother with it any more.'

I couldn't understand that bit at all, but I had one more question to get through to her.

'Why didn't the villains take the Bentley?'

'They took the Rover and the Wolsey, both in running order. The Bentley was up on blocks so they didn't bother. So she's the only one of my Things that I've got left, and I suppose that's why I'm so fond of her, though I know now that you shouldn't get fond of Things. How is she getting on?'

'Fine,' I answered. 'I just need a bit of help and, well, advice.'

'But of course,' she said. 'I'd give you a hand myself but I suppose I'm a bit past it. Look, the telephone's in the hall, at the end of that passage. Do use it if you need supplies. You haven't got relatives in New Zealand, I hope? I don't want you running up huge telephone bills.'

She'd said all that before. But I took the opportunity and went along that passageway again, found the telephone, and dialled my grandpa. He answered.

'Gramps,' I said. 'It's me, Jeff. You busy?'

'Of course. It's all go here. I was going to take Aunt Shirl for a drive.'

'Want a job, Gramps? I mean, can you help me out on one?'

'What sort of job, boy? I'll consider anything legal.'

'It's legal all right. I'm speaking from Rushby Manor.'

'Rushby Manor? What the blazes are you doing there?'

'I was, like, investigating a robbery and murder,

but that's all cleared up, and I'm working on this 1931 Bentley — '

'What's that? What's that? Jeff, I'm coming over straight away to see what you're up to. Don't do anything silly, boy! We'll be there in half an hour.'

That had fetched him!

As I hung up – yes, you actually hung the receiver onto a sort of fork – Trish joined me from the passage door. She looked worried.

'I feel a right wally, Trish,' I said. 'Giving you all that stuff about robbery and murder.'

She put an arm round me and rubbed against me like a pussycat.

'You were right to send for me, Jeff. There *was* a robbery, some time, and it's *horrible*, what they did. And Mrs Campbell could have died, lying there alone. What are we going to do with her?'

'What does she want to do?'

'She says she's perfectly all right here.'

'Let her stay then.'

'Don't be callous, Jeff. We can't leave her alone.'

'Who are we to push her about? And she won't be alone, there'll be me and there'll be my grandpa.'

'Not another geriatric!'

'He's a tough old bird. They'll get on well together. And it sounded like he was bringing auntie too.'

'Well,' she shrugged. 'Let me know this evening if there's any more trouble. I've got to get to school somehow. And what's my excuse for being late? They're so sticky, even with us sixth-formers.'

'I'll ring them and explain,' I said. 'What's their number?'

'Norwich 53265 – but no, you can't, Jeff! What are you going to say?'

'Don't you trust me?' I grinned as she tried to

139

snatch the phone from me. She let me dial and stood there biting her knuckles.

'School secretary?' I said down the mouthpiece. 'Rushby Manor Estate here. Security Officer speaking. It's about one of your girls, Patricia Niarchos-Jones . . . No, no . . . No trouble at all . . . Just helping with enquiries. She may miss a bit of school today . . . Yes, I have really appreciated her – er, her contact.'

I hung up again and we glared at each other.

'Quits?' I asked.

'Quits!' she giggled, and went all soft in my arms.

THE CONFIDENTIAL DIARY OF P. N-J

Saturday May 30th

. . . I must have done and said the right things with old Mrs Campbell, she was terribly gracious when I said goodbye and she said she hoped I would drop in whenever I felt like it. I think she means it. Jeff says I might as well move in with him, but . . . But what? He thinks nobody else need know, but what does he understand about living in a village like Rushby? *Everybody* would know. If I had parents I could run away from them, but I can't do that to the Joneses.

I got to school eventually by bike and bus and got some rather funny looks from my form mistress, but nobody asked any questions so Jeff's phone call must have worked.

Chantal muttered behind her book, with a leer, 'Been with that boy again?' I said I'd been making tea for an old lady, and I got another funny look.

A bit difficult to settle down to thinking about Interest, Probability and Risk (I wonder if the old lady's things were properly insured?).

Murder and robbery – they're things that happen in other people's lives, aren't they? I suppose I'm lucky to be able to say that. And I suppose Jeff can't see things that way. I'm just beginning to learn what it's like *not* wanting to dial 999. And there's still next Saturday hanging over us. It could be all in Jeff's mind, couldn't it, like today's murder? I do hope so.

9

Liberation!

At ten past three in the morning I was driving the Bentley carefully past the church and down the lane towards the stables. The early morning rabbits had to look out for themselves – we filled that lane from side to side.

I suppose I'd never have got her on the road without Gramp's help. We had some arguments about the supercharger. He wanted to take it off and fit standard carburettors, but I wasn't going to have that and between us we got the blower adjusted. We found some new tyres that fitted, and Mrs Campbell would get a hefty bill for parts. I took the car out onto the gravel drive once or twice before, all polished up, and the old lady was no end chuffed to see her. I had mastered the gears, more or less, and the pedals that had the accelerator in between the clutch and the brake. But it was really weird being out on the roads in this great heavy machine, like being in charge of a railway loco that had wandered off the rails. No worry about waking up the neighbours. I could hear the birds chirping above the purr of the engine.

The weather wasn't helping much. Instead of the bright moonlight I'd had the other time, a white mist had crept up from the marshes and was hanging halfway up the trees. I'd got the headlights on and they seemed to be running down the battery quicker than it was charging.

I steered into the farmyard, across the road from the stables. I didn't want to park where it would be noticed, but where do you hide a car that's fifteen feet long and weighs nearly two tons? I reversed it in alongside a giant combine harvester, which just about hid it from the road.

I walked across the road to the stables. The line of stalls stretched away in the dim misty light, with the faces of all my four-legged friends looking out. Outside Henry's stall stood a figure, female, long skirt, pigtails, headband, hippy style. Had the Animal Libbers got there before me? No, there was something about the way she stood. Yes, Trish in yet another of her disguises.

We met in a hug that was comforting rather than sexy.

'Oh, Jeff,' she breathed. 'Is it going to go all right? I couldn't stand it if anything happened to Henry. We should have sent for the police, the army, anything but those hippies.'

'You look a right hippy yourself,' I told her.

'I'm not sure it was a good idea. But it shows which side I'm on, I hope.'

We went and hid in the hay-barn, both of us too wound up to enjoy the soft bed. We waited, and listened for the sound of motors.

'What if the gang comes and not the Libbers?' she said. 'Or the Libbers and not the gang?'

'We'll play it by ear,' I said.

We strained our ears. The sound of a heavy diesel engine, approaching slowly. She grabbed my arm.

'That'll be the gang,' I whispered. 'Big cattle truck,

143

by the sound of it.' We stood up and squeezed hands. 'Stay here,' I told her, and walked out of the barn.

A huge cattle truck, that could take a whole herd of cows, was reversing slowly into the stable yard, its bleeper bleeping. It came to a stop. Tubby little Stan White climbed down from the cab, followed by Charlene. A hefty driver jumped down the other side. They went round to the rear and let down the ramp, and two other big fat men came down, holding sticks. I walked towards Stan and greeted him.

'Morning, Stan! Look, I've really sussed out these animals. Start at the far end. Lead that one on board – he'll be no trouble – then the rest will follow.'

'Good lad, Jeff! Like to start on that yourself?' Stan said.

'No, anyone can manage that one. I'll tell you about the difficult ones.' I knew I'd got to do the talking, and I had the advantage of knowing where I was. The others were staring about them, looking confused.

'Charlene, you bring the big 'un then,' Stan said to the girl. She glared at me and went off with a head-collar. I was a bit sorry for the girl, Nelson would soon deal with her.

I chose one of the fat plug-uglies I least liked the look of and said, 'I'll do you a favour, mate. Nice little mare in the centre stall. Ever so quiet. Slip a head-collar on her and she'll give you a kiss.'

He went happily into the stable of Lady the man-eater. Charlene, all smiles, was now leading Nelson towards the ramp. He was so quiet that I thought he might let me down and walk aboard. But no, he jammed on the brakes, snuffed and snorted; the girl tried to tug him onward and swore; he went hard into reverse and backed towards the muckheap, dragging Charlene. He plunged his head down, whipped round, and bolted off towards the misty marsh. The girl – she did know a thing or two – let go just in time. At that moment there came shouts and curses from Lady's stall, and the fat man came bolting out, rubbing his wrist and shouting, 'That bugger bites!'

Stan White stood in the centre of the yard and lost his temper. 'Have I got a bunch of wets here? Charlene, I thought you knew about horses! Kevin and Dale, stop poncing around and get behind them animals with a stick. This ain't no Pets Corner, geddit? And I'm givin' the orders, not you, Jeff Dooley! Let's see you drive 'em on board, and less of your advice! Get hold of that other big 'un, Dale, he's got the meat on him.'

Yes, I was afraid they would get hold of Tiny, who was huge, half carthorse, and would do anything for anybody. I'd won the first round. Had I lost the match? Where were those Animal Libbers?

The two toughs were dragging and thumping Tiny towards the truck, though he didn't need beating. Charlene was leading out little old Soldier, the beginners pony. There was nothing to stop them being put on board.

I'd lost! I looked round for Trish but she was nowhere to be seen. Stan White saw me standing there.

'Get moving then, Jeff Dooley! Let's see you get one of your little friends on board, if you know so much about them!'

I thought I'd better show willing so I went and collected poor old Chalky the OAP. It might even be kinder if he was turned into catsmeat. As I led him past Henry's stall, I saw Trish's white face peering through a crack in the half door.

'Jeff!' she hissed, horrified and distracted. 'Whose side do you think you're *on*?'

And then suddenly the yard was full of people. A *lot* of people. They seemed to come out of the mist. Girls in long skirts and sandals, big chunky beardies, bald-headed men with spectacles and tweed suits, quite small kids running about, and wild uncontrolled hairy dogs yapping hoarsely. Some of the people carried cardboard banners saying STOP THIS CRUELTY! and SET THE BEASTS FREE! Wild young men were running to the occupied stables, throwing them open and shouting, 'You're free! You're free!' to the wide-eyed horses cowering in the corners. One of the hippy girls was for some reason trying to stop them. Of course! That was Trish! Somebody wrenched the leading rope from my hand and pulled the head-collar off old Chalky, who stood there mildly surprised. A girl in sensible dungarees was calling out in a loud, clear voice, 'THESE ANIMALS ARE EXPLOITED AND DEPRAVED!' Ah, that was Fiona.

But another voice, Stan's, was bellowing, 'Take no notice of them bleeding hippies! Get the beasts aboard!' I could see the two hoodlums threatening girls with their cattle sticks.

And then *BANG!*

A bomb?

'What bloody fool threw a firework? We said no fireworks!' one of the bearded men shouted. But the thunderflash had done its work. Even old Chalky reared up and bolted. Tiny bolted out to the marsh, kicking out with his heels at somebody as he passed. I was glad to see it was Stan White that got it. Three other horses followed Tiny. Soldier and two more bolted out onto the road. There was not a horse to be seen in the yard. A stream of curses from Stan, then he shouted, 'Jack it in, everyone! Everyone on board!' And the truck moved out of the yard, children and dogs scattering in front of it.

The gang had gone, and we'd won! But a desperate Trish was fighting her way through the crowd to me.

'Jeff! Jeff!' she sobbed furiously. 'They've gone off with Henry! He was on board that truck! You let them do it!'

I grabbed her by the arm and said, 'The Bentley!' She resisted, but I hauled her along. I dragged her across the road and into the farmyard, and she gasped to see the Bentley standing there.

'Get in!' I ordered. 'We can catch them!'

She hesitated, but only for a moment. Then she jumped on the running-board and climbed in the passenger seat and I jumped in the other side. The engine started at a touch – I hadn't spent all that time tuning for nothing – I slammed in the gear and we bumped down the farmyard. At the road Trish grabbed my arm.

'Don't follow them, Jeff! Go the long way round and cut them off! Can this thing go fast?'

I didn't argue, I was too busy driving, but I knew these *things* used to do 130 miles an hour. As soon as we got away from the houses and corners I put my foot down. There was a whine like a power-drill – I'd never heard a supercharger in action before. Long Road is a half-mile straight and we must have done it in 20 seconds. It took all my strength to drag her round the 90 degree left hand turn at the top. She skidded but she was too massive to roll. Yarmouth Road is pretty straight, too, and Trish kept saying 'Faster! Faster!' and 'Come *on*, Joy!'. If anything had been coming ahead – I don't like to think of it, you don't stop two tons in a hurry. But it was still early dawn and the roads were empty. There was the T junction ahead, and the church.

147

'Left or right, Trish?'

'*Left!*' she shouted. 'Oh God, I hope I'm right!'

'Did you say left or right?'

'Left! Left!'

I nearly left it too late and demolished the church. We were in the narrow lane.

'Slow down, Jeff! And stop here!'

I braked and we came to a stop. Then I saw what she was after. There are about six hills on the Norfolk roads and Turkeycock Hill is one of them. It may not be the highest or steepest but it's probably the narrowest, with banks straight up on both sides and not a hope of two minis passing each other, let alone a cattle truck and a Bentley. I stopped at the top, had a thought, and grabbed my chauffeur's cap and jacket from the back seat and quickly put them on. Then I reached for the black crash-helmet and goggles and pushed them onto Trish's head. Climbing out of the mist, round the bend of the steep lane, came the mass of the cattle truck. It slowed, and the driver blew his horn furiously. It stopped. I pulled my dark uniform cap down over my face, but I could lip-read Stan's words behind the windscreen of the truck.

'The cops!'

We must have looked like the Sweeney's secret weapon at top of the hill there in our massive black machine with the supercharger aimed at them, and us in our dark uniform hats. Trish was going to get out but I held her back. We sat still, and had a front row view of the fun as first of all the driver bailed out, scrambled up the bank, and stumbled off down the steep field towards Haddiscoe marshes. Stan followed, limping and cursing. The girl Charlene – you've got to hand it to her – squeezed round to the rear of the truck and let the two fatties out, who followed the first two over the bank. Charlene stayed on board.

'What's she doing with my Henry?' Trish wailed, and hurled herself out of the car. I followed her round to the rear of the truck. There was Henry, poised at the top of the ramp, looking around and sniffing the air, with Charlene on the end of the leading rope. I don't know what she thought she was going to do with him – mount him bareback and make a quick getaway?

She wasn't quick enough. Henry did one of his lightning exits down the ramp and pulled Charlene over onto her face in the lane. Henry broke free, but stopped calmly at the bank and munched cow parsley. Trish walked up to him, crooning gently. I went for Charlene, but I was glad enough when she scrambled to her feet and disappeared over the bank. One girl was enough for me.

Trish's tear-smudged face smiled at me over Henry's neck, a bit shyly.

'Jeff, I'm sorry. I didn't trust you, for a bit. I wasn't sure which side you were on. Forgive me?'

'That's all right, Trish. Don't blame you. I nearly screwed it all up. Is Henry all right?'

'He'll be OK. Oh, Henry darling, it would have to be you who they got on board! You just love going places, don't you? Well, you're going home, see? I'll lead him home, Jeff. It's not that far and the walk will quieten us both down.'

'Are you sure you'll be all right, you two?'

'Sure. Will you be? What are you going to do with this bloody truck?'

'I'll think of something. 'Bye!'

I watched them go, Trish having difficulty with her long hippy skirt. I climbed into the cab of the truck. A few papers in the dash shelf. One or two of them

149

were even headed SPACEWIDE TRANSPORT, Prop.
S White. Should I take them away, as evidence? No,
leave them here, as evidence. Hide them where they
wouldn't take too much finding – the police were
going to search this abandoned vehicle. But supposing
Stan and Co changed their minds and came back?
Why should they get away with the truck? I got out
and looked at the tyres. It would take too long to let
the air out of the valves. I went to the back of the
Bentley where I had my toolkit, and took out a Stanley knife. There you go, Stanley! I was sorry for those
innocent tyres as the air rushed out of them – no, I
really don't enjoy damaging things. But I wasn't sorry
for Stanley White, when I thought of all the worry
he had caused my Trish, and the worse agonies he
had planned for her.

I backed the Bentley up towards the T-junction,
and I thought she had done her bit so I drove her
back to the manor and left her in the coach house. I
would need to hose the farmyard mud off the wheels
and body, but not now. I looked at my watch. It
wasn't yet five o'clock. The sun was just getting above
the mist as I walked across the fields to the stables.

Music? It sort of fitted the misty morning, a
squeaky piping tone, quite nice. Apart from that all
was quiet, very quiet. A smell of gunpowder was the
only thing to remind me of the battle. The stables
were all empty except for Henry's. All the other doors
swung open, and so did the field gate to the marsh.

And there was this girl in hippy dress – Trish of
course – with a girl in dungarees. Fiona! Nobody else.
Why weren't they scratching each other's eyes out?
They weren't. Trish was mixing feed in a black vinyl
trough, with her two plaits hanging down, while
Fiona sat on a straw bale watching her and playing
on her penny-whistle.

150

Fiona stopped playing, looked round and saw me.

'Oh, Jeff!' she said. 'You never said this was the place where Trish works!'

'Are you two friends then?' I asked. I never like it much when girl friends and ex-girl-friends get together. They compare notes, don't they?

Trish looked up from her mixing bowl with a grin. 'Yes, Jeff, we're still friends, Feef and me. She doesn't really believe we're grateful for bringing the demo along. We are grateful to Fiona, aren't we, Henry? And to Joy.'

Henry snuffled over the half door and kicked it.

'All right, all right, breakfast's coming,' Trish said. 'You don't *mind* if I put off his liberation until after his breakfast?' she teased Fiona. 'They always go out on the marsh meadows, anyhow.'

Fiona made a face. 'I suppose I was wrong, shouting all those slogans here. I'm sorry, Trish.'

'Not at all, Feef, you were dead right. THESE ANIMALS ARE EXPLOITED AND DEPRAVED! Watch this!' Trish stood up with the bowl and approached Henry's stable. 'Stand back, you depraved beast, Henry!' She pushed him back by his nose as he snuffled and danced, she opened the door and dumped the feed bowl onto the stable floor. He pushed his nose into it.

'How depraved can you get, eh? And if I don't exploit you for more than a couple of hours a week you'll get really fat, won't you, Henry? No, Fiona, I think Animal Lib's just a bit late to save horses. You might have saved them from exploitation a few thousand years ago. What's this, now?'

There were sounds of slow hoofbeats. Nelson was wandering in from the marsh. From the direction of the road came Soldier. Nelson stood there on three legs, begging.

'See what I mean?' said Trish. 'They'll do anything for a bowl of hossmix. Get head-collars on those two and put them in their stalls, will you, Jeff love? You've just gotta love 'em and ride 'em, Fiona.'

'Are you talking about men or horses?' Fiona asked.

'Both, I suppose,' said Trish.

THE CONFIDENTIAL DIARY OF P. N-J

Wednesday, June 3rd

What sort of exams do horses take?
Hay levels.

OK, Niarchos-Jones, if you think that's funny you really have smashed your tiny mind with all that revising.

A level Maths tomorrow. *Remember to take:*
Pen
Pencils
Spare pen
Spare cartridges (for Russian roulette!)
Ink eraser
Geometry set
Tissues (for mopping tears of despair)
Brains (if any)
                    Try to forget:
That this is the Big Event. 'Take it easy, Henry, we're going to pretend we're just practising in the paddock, aren't we?' (I bet he never believed that either.)

Hay levels, feed levels – 'Forget about it,' says darling Jeff. 'I'll look after Henry.' So things do work out together. Sometimes. Hopefully.

Of course he can manage. Any fool can feed a horse and muck out. Jeff even says he will take Henry for an exercise walk, on a string like a doggie.

I've told my Examination Counsellor I've arranged for my horse to be looked after by the groom-chauffeur at the Manor. She agreed it was wise of me to hand over my responsibilities to a reliable person like that so I can concentrate on keeping a clear mind! If only she *knew!*

Forget about feeling jealous of Jeff and Henry, out in the sunshine together!